A DICTIONARY OF SPECTROSCOPY

A DICTIONARY OF SPECTROSCOPY

R. C. DENNEY
B.Sc., Ph.D., F.R.I.C.

Senior Lecturer in Chemistry, Thames Polytechnic, London

MACMILLAN
PERKIN-ELMER

First published 1973 by
THE MACMILLAN PRESS LTD
London and Basingstoke
Associated companies in New York Dublin
Melbourne Johannesburg and Madras

SBN 333 13880 5

Distributed in the U.S.A. and Canada
by Halsted Press, a division of
John Wiley & Sons, Inc., New York

Library of Congress catalog card number: 73–10600

Text set in 10/12pt. Monotype Times New Roman,
printed by photolithography, and bound in
Great Britain at The Pitman Press, Bath

To the highly charged particle in a box—our son Graham

Acknowledgements

The writer of a scientific book can rarely operate within a vacuum. If his final product is to attain a level of reliability, he must frequently call upon the assistance of others who have superior knowledge in certain fields. I am always conscious of the considerable debt that I owe other people when a book is finally completed. Without considerable encouragement and active help from many friends and associates the work would be more difficult and the final product of a lower standard. During the preparation of this particular book I have greatly appreciated the interest of many colleagues at Thames Polytechnic who considered my idea so worth while.

I am indebted to Dr. M. A. Ford and Mr. E. G. Cummins of Perkin–Elmer Ltd. for their continual enthusiasm and assistance. Most of the admirable diagrams throughout the length of the book have been included thanks to their cooperation and hard work in obtaining suitable illustrations to match the text.

I am especially grateful to my very good friend John Mendham, A.R.I.C., for advising me on aspects of emission and atomic absorption spectroscopy, and to Dr. C. W. N. Cumper, D.Sc., who made many useful suggestions for improving the text and advised me on symbols and nomenclature. I remain, however, solely responsible for any errors that remain in the text.

Finally I would like to thank my wife for once again tolerating the many evenings and weekends that I have spent working in libraries and slaving over a hot typewriter.

Sources of Diagrams

Perkin–Elmer Limited, Beaconsfield, Buckinghamshire, England kindly drew and provided the following diagrams: figures 1, 2, 5, 6, 7, 9, 12, 13, 16, 17, 19, 21, 22, 23, 24, 25, 26, 27, 31, 32, 33, 34, 35, 36, 37, 38, 39, 40, 41, 44, 45, 46, 47.

Figure 10 is included by kind permission of Rank Precision Industries Ltd. (Hilger and Watts, Analytical Division), and figure 11 by kind permission of AEI Scientific Apparatus Ltd. Figures 28 and 42 have been reproduced from *Chemical Spectroscopy*, 2nd edition, 1943, published by John Wiley, by permission of the author Professor W. R. Brode. Figure 29 has been reproduced from *Chemistry in Britain* by permission of the editor and the approval of the author Dr. W. McFarlane.

All other diagrams are the copyright of Dr. Ronald C. Denney.

Introduction

During the years that I have been lecturing on various aspects of spectroscopy I have felt that there has become a growing need for a relatively simple reference book dealing with the individual items in the spectroscopic field. Frequently a student, or worker, in a spectroscopic subject requires a quick answer to the meaning or inter-relationship of a spectroscopic term. All too often he can only find this by wading through many pages of a standard textbook on the subject. This is particularly so in the confusing areas of symbols, nomenclature and terminology in which lack of uniformity still persists.

By collecting together the most common expressions, equations and terms used in spectroscopy in alphabetical form I have tried to construct what I hope will be a useful reference source intended to save a great deal of time for many people.

Throughout the book I have tried to standardize and update the symbols and nomenclature. As far as possible these are based upon the recommendations of the Symbols Committee of the Royal Society[1] and of those adopted by the International Union of Pure and Applied Chemistry[2] employing SI units. In a few instances I have chosen to adhere to accepted terminology where there has been no obvious preference for a new name or expression, or where there have been counter recommendations and no real standardization.

In its present form the book has been limited in size and some of the newer areas of spectroscopy have only been touched on. This is because the book is intended for the general spectroscopist and undergraduate not the specialist. The field of x-ray spectroscopy has been omitted as that deserves a book of this size all to itself.

Where appropriate, headings dealing with dimensions or constants are followed by the corresponding symbol, e.g. hertz Hz. Also, many headings are followed by an abbreviation in parentheses indicating the main, but not necessarily exclusive, realm of spectroscopy to which it applies. For this purpose the following abbreviations are used:

(a.s.)   atomic
(em.)   emission

Introduction

(e.s.r.)	electron spin resonance
(i.r.)	infrared
(m.s.)	mass
(n.m.r.)	nuclear magnetic resonance
(pl.)	photoluminescence
(r.s.)	Raman
(u.v.)	ultraviolet/visible

I would be pleased to receive suggestions for improvement or for further inclusions in the hope that these might be incorporated in any further edition of the book

Ronald C. Denney
September 1973

Symbols

The following symbols and letters are employed in the equations throughout the book:

A	ampere	M	magnetization
A	absorbance	m	metre
Å	ångström	m	mass
A_r	atomic mass of an element	m_e	mass of electron at rest
a	absorption coefficient	m_i	magnetic quantum number
B	magnetic flux density	m_p	mass of proton at rest
c	molar concentration	mm	millimetre
c	speed of light in a vacuum	N	number of molecules in the ground state
cm	centimetre		
E	energy	N_A	Avogadro constant
e	base of natural logarithms	N_E	number of molecules with energy E
e	elementary charge		
f	force constant	n	refractive index
g	Landé factor	n	spectrum order
H	henry (inductance)	nm	nanometre
H	magnetic field strength	P	probability
H_1	radio-frequency field amplitude	Pa	pascal
		Q	quadrupole moment
h	Planck constant	R	gas constant
I	intensity of transmitted light	R_H	Rydberg constant for hydrogen
I	spin quantum number		
I_0	intensity of incident light	R_∞	Rydberg constant (heavy atom)
J	joule		
J	coupling constant	r	path radius
K	kelvin	r_s	distance from scattering particle
k	Boltzmann constant		
l	cell path length	T	tesla
l	time-of-flight path length	T	temperature
M	mass of nucleus	T	transmittance
M	radiant exitance	T_1	longitudinal relaxation time

Symbols

T_2	transverse relaxation time	μ_N	nuclear magneton
T_s	spin temperature	μ_0	permeability of vacuum
t	time	μ_r	relative permeability
V	volt	ν	frequency
v	velocity	$\bar{\nu}$	wavenumber
Z	charge on the nucleus	π	ratio of circumference to diameter of circle
α	polarizability	ρ_N	depolarization factor
γ	magnetogyric ratio	σ	nuclear screening constant
δ	chemical shift	σ	standard deviation
ε	molar extinction coefficient	σ	Stefan–Boltzmann constant
θ	angular measurement	τ	chemical shift
λ	wavelength	Φ	magnetic flux
μ	magnetic moment of particle	χ_m	magnetic susceptibility
μ	permeability	Ψ	eigenfunction
μ	statistical mean	ω_L	Larmor (angular) frequency
μ	micro	ω_N	nuclear angular precession frequency
μ_B	Bohr magneton		

Greek Alphabet

As so many spectroscopic equations include the use of Greek letters the following alphabet has been included to help the reader to give the correct name to these letters as they arise in the text:

alpha	A	α	nu	N	ν
beta	B	β	xi	Ξ	ξ
gamma	Γ	γ	omicron	O	o
delta	Δ	δ	pi	Π	π
epsilon	E	ε	rho	P	ρ
zeta	Z	ζ	sigma	Σ	σ
eta	H	η	tau	T	τ
theta	Θ	θ	upsilon	Y	υ
iota	I	ι	phi	Φ	ϕ
kappa	K	κ	chi	X	χ
lambda	Λ	λ	psi	Ψ	ψ
mu	M	μ	omega	Ω	ω

A

A bands (u.v.)
Various systems of nomenclature for ultraviolet spectra have designated different absorption groups as A bands. Moser and Kohlenberg[3] used it to refer to the bands occurring at the shortest-wavelength region.
see Bands (ultraviolet)

Abscissa
This is the name given to the horizontal axis in a set of two-dimensional coordinates. Frequently this is referred to as the X axis, so that the abscissa of any point in the plane of the two axes forming the coordinates is the value at the point on the X axis at which a vertical line from the point meets that axis.
see also Ordinate

Absorbance A
The absorbance for a material is the logarithm of the ratio of the intensities of the incident light and the transmitted light. Its value can be calculated from the molar extinction coefficient (q.v.), the thickness (in cm) and the molar concentration of the material.

$$A = \log_{10} \frac{I_0}{I} = \varepsilon l c = \log_{10} \frac{1}{T}$$

The term absorbance has been recommended for use in preference to absorbancy, optical density or extinction[4].
see also Beer–Lambert law

Absorbancy
see Absorbance

Absorption
Transitions from low energy states to higher energy states within molecular and atomic systems occur as a result of absorption of electromagnetic

1

radiation. Changes in electronic energy levels are measured by absorption of ultraviolet/visible radiation; changes in vibrational energy levels occur by absorption of infrared radiation and changes in nuclear energy levels by absorption of radio-frequency radiation.

Similarly the absorption of microwave radiation (q.v.) is used to study transitions between electron spin energy levels in electron spin resonance spectroscopy (q.v.).

Absorption band

This is any region of the absorption spectrum in which the absorbance (q.v.) includes a maximum.

see also Bands (infrared); Bands (ultraviolet)

Absorption coefficient *a*

see Extinction coefficient

Absorption spectrum

A record of the absorbance (q.v.) or transmittance (q.v.) of a material with respect to wavelength or some function of the wavelength. This may be manually plotted or automatically recorded.

Absorptivity

see Extinction coefficient

Absorptivity *M*

see Molar extinction coefficient

Abundance tables (m.s.)

These are lists of molecular formulae, usually limited to compounds containing carbon, hydrogen, oxygen and nitrogen, showing the relative sizes of the $P + 1$ and $P + 2$ peaks to the parent peak (q.v.) for each formula. These particular peaks arise from the existence of the heavier isotopes in the molecules and their sizes are related to the number of each atomic species present. These tables[5] are now based upon $^{12}C = 12 \cdot 0000$; earlier tables were based upon $^{16}O = 16 \cdot 0000$.

see also Isotopic abundance

2

a.c. arc source (em.)
Voltages below 5000 V are employed in this method of vaporization and excitation in emission spectroscopy. The arc is struck between an electrode gap of about 2·5 mm with a current of 2 to 5 A. Results are more reproducible than with the d.c. arc (q.v.). The a.c. arc source is considered a compromise between the poor sensitivity, high selectivity of the a.c. spark source (q.v.) and the high sensitivity, poor selectivity of the d.c. arc source. It is used particularly with zinc and other non-ferrous metal alloys, although it tends to give a greater cyanogen background from the atmosphere than does the a.c. spark source.

Accelerating slits (m.s.)
Positively charged ions produced in the ionization chamber of a mass spectrometer are passed into the analyser of the instrument by the accelerating slits. For this purpose two accelerating slits are employed. The first is at a slight negative potential with respect to the ionization chamber in order to attract the positive ions from the source. The real acceleration occurs as a result of the powerful electrostatic field of up to 8000 V between the first and second slits which leads to ion velocities of up to 150 000 m s^{-1} being produced. As a result the ions possess identical kinetic energies but different velocities; as given by the equation

$$eV = \tfrac{1}{2}m_1v_1{}^2 = \tfrac{1}{2}m_2v_2{}^2 = \tfrac{1}{2}m_3v_3{}^2, \text{etc.}$$

Achromatic lens
A transparent substance is said to be achromatic when it has the ability of transmitting light without dispersing it into its constituent colours. Thus, an achromatic lens will produce images which do not have rainbow-coloured edges. This is achieved by forming the lens from two materials possessing different refractive indices such that the dispersion (q.v.) due to one material is corrected by the dispersion due to the other. In practice the correction is only absolute at two selected wavelengths, some slight dispersion remaining for the other wavelengths in the spectrum. Crown glass and flint glass are the most common combination for this purpose.

a.c. spark source (em.)
This is the preferred type of source for high-precision emission spectroscopy, particularly for producing ionic spectra. The spark is produced from a

3

transformer, capable of operating as high as 50 kV, connected in parallel with a condenser across the spark gap. The heating effect of the spark source is less than that of either the a.c. or the d.c. arc sources (q.v.) and is used for studying low-melting solids and liquids. Graphite electrodes are usually used and the spark energy provides the excitation energy necessary for electronic transitions to take place.

Adiabatic ionization energy (m.s.)

see Ionization energy

Analyser tube (m.s.)

The analyser tube in a mass spectrometer is the section of the instrument in which positive ions are separated according to their mass/charge ratios. The operating pressure for the tube is about 10^{-5} to 10^{-6} Pa (10^{-7} to 10^{-8} torr). In mass spectrometers using electrostatic and magnetic fields the analyser tube is curved and almost completely enclosed by the fields; in time-of-flight instruments (q.v.) the tube is straight.

see also Field-free region

Ångström Å

It is defined as the unit of length equal to $1/6438 \cdot 4696$ of the wavelength of the red line of cadmium.

$$1 \text{ Å} = 10^{-10} \text{ m} = 10^{-8} \text{ cm}$$

The ångström has been a useful dimension for representing interatomic distances; however, it is not an SI unit (q.v.) and is likely to drop from usage as these units are progressively adopted.

Anisotopic (m.s.)

An element is said to be anisotopic when it possesses only one naturally occurring isotope. Fluorine is a typical anisotopic element and mass spectra of molecules containing fluorine atoms are more simple than are those of corresponding chlorine and bromine compounds.

Anisotropy (n.m.r.)

see Diamagnetic anisotropy

4

Anode (m.s.)
The positive electrode in an electron tube or electron ionization chamber is called the anode and acts as a collector for the electrons and any negatively charged particles. It therefore operates at a positive potential with respect to the cathode (q.v.). In the ionization chambers of mass spectrometers the anode is known as the 'trap' and is made from a robust metal such as stainless steel.

Anti-bonding orbitals (u.v.)
see Bonding orbitals

Anti-Stokes fluorescence (pl.)
Although most fluorescent species comply with the Stokes law (q.v.), a weak fluorescence found at a shorter wavelength than the exciting wavelength is also sometimes observed at room temperature. This anti-Stokes fluorescence derives its additional energy from excited vibrational levels within the ground state[6].

Anti-Stokes lines (r.s.)
These are the Raman lines measured on the shorter-wavelength side of the monochromatic radiation source. They arise from those Raman transitions in which the final vibration level is lower than the initial vibration level. The anti-Stokes lines in Raman spectroscopy are much weaker than are the corresponding Stokes lines (q.v.) occurring at longer wavelengths; for this reason the latter spectrum is preferentially scanned.
see Raman spectroscopy

Appearance potential (m.s.)
Fragmentation ions in a mass spectrum do not occur until the ionization energy (q.v.) for the molecule has been exceeded. In general the appearance potential for the most readily formed fragment ions is about 1 to 4 eV higher than the value for the ionization energy of the corresponding molecular ion.

Astigmatic
Optical systems in spectrometers are said to be astigmatic when the focal point for the vertical image occurs at a different position from that for the

5

horizontal image. This is a problem that occurs with many forms of diffraction grating mounts.

Atomic absorption spectroscopy (a.s.)

A very sensitive method of spectroscopy for elemental analysis in which the sample is converted into the atomic state by combustion in a flame. This produces pure electronic transitions free from vibrational and rotational transitions. The number of atoms capable of absorbing any particular wavelength of transmitted light is proportional to the concentration of these atoms in the flame and to the length of the path in the flame. The radiant source employed for atomic absorption spectroscopy is a hollow cathode lamp (q.v.) emitting radiation from excited atoms of the same element as that to be determined.

The hollow cathode source emits energy, in the form of a line spectrum,

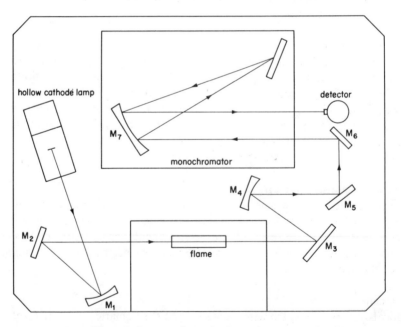

Figure 1. Layout of atomic absorption spectrometer

6

which is absorbed by the sample in the flame. This produces a spectrum of the source radiation with lines of reduced intensity. The magnitude of the reduction of intensity is related to the number of atoms of the element in the flame. The monochromator in the instrument is used to select a single wavelength for examination and changes in the intensity of this wavelength are related to different concentrations of the nebulized sample[7].

Atomic absorption is a rapidly expanding field[8], and recent developments include the introduction of flameless atomic absorption devices, known collectively as atom reservoirs (q.v.), which have enhanced the sensitivity of the technique.

see also Electrodeless discharge tube

Atomic spectra

Transitions between electronic energy levels within atoms lead to the emission or absorption of radiation in a series of sharply defined lines corresponding to fixed wavelengths representing radiation quanta of definite energies. Of the five series of lines for hydrogen that in the visible region was the first discovered, by J. J. Balmer[9]. The formula for the relationship between the frequency of the radiation (v) and the energy level transitions is given by

$$v = R_H \left(\frac{1}{n_1{}^2} - \frac{1}{n_2{}^2} \right)$$

The values of n_1 and n_2 for the hydrogen series are given by table 1.

Table 1

Series	n_1	n_2	Region
Lyman	1	2, 3, 4, . . .	far u.v.
Balmer	2	3, 4, 5, . . .	visible
Paschen	3	4, 5, 6, . . .	far i.r.
Brackett	4	5, 6, 7, . . .	far i.r.
Pfund	5	6, 7, 8, . . .	far i.r.

The general formula for hydrogen like spectra (produced from ions such as He^+, Li^{2+}, Be^{3+}) is

$$v = RZ^2 \left(\frac{1}{n_1{}^2} - \frac{1}{n_2{}^2} \right)$$

The value for the Rydberg constant (q.v.) in each case being determined from R_∞.

Atomizer (a.s.)
In spectroscopy the word atomizer is used specifically for the instrumental region in which free atoms are released. In atomic absorption spectroscopy (q.v.) this refers to the flame or carbon filament (q.v.), whereas the formation of liquid droplets is carried out by the nebulizer (q.v.).

Atom reservoirs (a.s.)
    see Carbon filament atom reservoir; Delves cup;
       Massmann furnace; Tantalum boat

A.T.R. (i.r.)
       see Attenuated total reflectance

Attenuated total reflectance
An infrared spectroscopic technique used particularly for examining opaque solids, in which the sample is placed against the face of a prism[10]. Radiant energy passing through the wall of the prism is selectively reflected

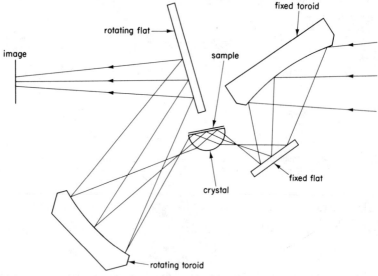

Figure 2. Arrangement for attenuated total reflectance

by the sample, having only penetrated it by a few micrometres. The refractive index of the sample must be less than that of the prism and a good optical contact between the sample and prism must be maintained. For attenuated total reflectance to occur it is necessary to use a fixed angle of incidence that is greater than the critical angle. The prism (or hemicylinder) may be silver chloride, silicon or KRS-5 (q.v.)[11] as these possess refractive indices > 2. Spectra obtained by this procedure are similar to ordinary absorption spectra.

Attenuator (e.s.r.)
Attenuation of the microwave power passing along a waveguide (q.v.) is achieved by means of a metal plate placed along the axis of the waveguide. The degree of attenuation increases as the plate is moved away from the wall of the waveguide towards the centre.

Attenuator (i.r., u.v.)
A toothed comb, grid or star wheel arrangement introduced into one beam of a spectrophotometer, operated either automatically through an electronic servosystem, or manually to balance the radiation in both beams.
see also Optical null principle

Auer burner (i.r.)
This is one of the sources of radiation suitable for far-infrared spectroscopy. The radiation is emitted from a thorium oxide mantle heated to 1800 °C by burning gas. Its optimum operating region is around 50 µm, above this a quartz mercury lamp is used.

Auger effect
This is the name given to radiationless reorganization that can occur within ions that have been formed by loss of an inner shell electron from neutral atoms. The reorganization takes place by a higher-level electron filling the inner shell vacancy and in so doing transferring its energy to another electron which is ejected. This ejected electron is known as the Auger electron. The paths of ejected electrons are followed by cloud-chamber photographs.

Auxochromes (u.v.)
Certain chemical groups substituted into molecules have been found to cause a change in the wavelength and magnitude of the characteristic

9

absorptions arising from chromophores (q.v.). These groups are called auxochromes and do not themselves usually absorb above 200 nm. Typical auxochromes are found to possess non-bonding electrons (q.v.); such as $-OH$, $-NH_2$ and $-SH$. It is considered that the auxochrome functions by a charge transfer mechanism[12], the auxochrome acting as a donor of charge during the electronic transition of electrons in an adjacent bond.

see also Bathochromic shift; Hyperchromic effect

Avogadro constant L or N_A
The number of molecules in 1 mole of any substance, currently given as $6\cdot022\ 169 \times 10^{23}$ mole^{-1}.

Axis of symmetry (i.r.)
When a molecule can be rotated about any axis passing through it to produce a molecular arrangement indistinguishable from the original position it is said to possess an axis of symmetry. If such a situation occurs for a rotation of $360°/2 = 180°$ it is said to be a two-fold axis of symmetry, and if for every $360°/3 = 120°$ it is a three-fold axis of symmetry. Linear molecules possess an ∞-fold axis of symmetry.

see also Centre of symmetry; Plane of symmetry

B

Balmer series (em.)

see Atomic spectra

Bandpass filter
In spectrophotometers incorporating diffraction gratings (q.v.) it is necessary to ensure that only first-order spectra are obtained. The bandpass filter is incorporated into the optical system to remove the higher-order spectra. It consists of two filters, one giving an increase in transmission from longer to shorter wavelength, the other giving the increase in transmission from shorter to longer wavelength. The useful region is, therefore, restricted to that portion in which the transmission ranges of the two filters overlap.

Bandpass width
       see Effective bandwidth

Bands (infrared)
Spectra in the middle-infrared region consist of absorptions arising from vibrational transitions in molecules accompanied by rotational transitions. Complete resolution of the fine structure due to individual rotational transitions in this region can be carried out for gaseous samples. For liquid or solid samples infrared bands have the broad outline of the vibrational transition envelope.
       see also Infrared spectra

Bands (ultraviolet)
Ultraviolet absorption spectra of conjugated organic compounds are considered to arise from four main electronic transition types giving rise to broad absorption bands. In order to establish some relationship between absorption bands from different compounds several classifications of these bands have been made and were summarized by Forbes and Shilton[13] (table 2). The system due to Moser and Kohlenberg has been frequently recommended as the alphabetical order is consistent with increasing wavelength.

Table 2. Absorption bands

increasing wavelength ⟶

Burawoy[14] and Braude[15] Doub and Vandenbelt[16]	— 2nd primary band	K and E 3rd primary band	B secondary band	R —
Klevens and Platt[17]	A and B	C	D	—
Moser and Kohlenberg[13]	A	B	C	D
Clar[18]	β	P	α	—

Inorganic compounds of transition metal ions and their complexes also undergo electronic transitions giving rise to ultraviolet/visible spectra. These are currently explained by ligand field theory (q.v.).

Bandwidth
       see Effective bandwidth

11

Bar

see Pressure, units

Bar graph (m.s.)
A diagrammatic presentation of a mass spectrum using a linear mass/charge scale and in which the various spectral peaks are represented by vertical lines with lengths corresponding to the relative abundancies of the individual ions expressed as percentages with reference to the most abundant ion (*see* Base peak).

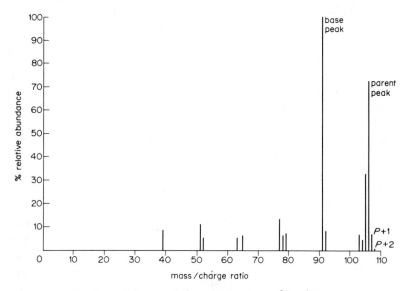

Figure 3. Bar graph for mass spectrum of p-xylene

Barrier-layer cell (u.v., a.s.)
This photoelectric detector system consists of a thin film of silver covering a layer of semiconductor, usually selenium, deposited upon an iron base. After passing through the silver film the radiation falling on the semi-conductor leads to the release of electrons at the selenium–silver interface and these pass to the silver layer which acts as a collector electrode. The area of contact between the conducting metal and the semiconductor is the barrier layer.

Base-line method (i.r.)

In quantitative analysis one of the major difficulties in measuring absorbance values is the very irregular base line. To overcome this problem an arbitrary line may be chosen to represent the base line for the absorption band (q.v.) being employed for the measurement[19]. In practice the base line is usually drawn as a tangent to two adjacent absorption minima and the vertical distance from this line to the absorption maximum is the measurement employed in the quantitative calculation. The method has been used for the quantitative analysis of mixtures[20] by infrared spectroscopy and may also be applied in other realms of spectroscopy.

Base peak (m.s.)

The most intense peak in a mass spectrum is referred to as the base peak. It is normally given the arbitrary value of 100 in order that all other peaks may be expressed as a percentage of the base peak (*see* Bar graph). The parent (or molecular) peak (q.v.) is not necessarily the base peak as in most mass spectra it is not the most intense peak obtained. Frequently the base peak is that obtained for a fragment ion formed by loss of a small portion of the parent molecule.

Batch inlet sampling system (m.s.)

The purpose of the batch inlet system for a mass spectrometer is to enable a volatile sample to be continuously fed into the ionization chamber without having to add repeated small amounts of sample. For this purpose the main sample, contained in a tube that can be cooled in liquid nitrogen, is allowed to expand into a large reservoir of up to 1 litre capacity. From here it is gradually bled through a leak valve (q.v.) into the ionization chamber. The reservoir is maintained at a pressure of 10^{-5} to 10^{-6} torr whilst the mass spectrometer is kept at about 10^{-7} to 10^{-8} torr. By this means the spectra of gases and volatile liquids can be obtained without the risk of either spoiling the vacuum in the instrument or overloading the ionization chamber. Once the material from the reservoir has been exhausted a further amount of sample can be expanded from the cooled sample tube.

see also Direct inlet system; Direct insertion probe

Bathochromic shift (u.v.)

When structural modification in a molecule leads to a characteristic absorption maximum shifted to a longer wavelength (lower frequency) it is

B bands (*u.v.*)

said to have caused a bathochromic shift. This is sometimes referred to as a red shift, as the displacement is in the direction of the red end of the visible spectrum.

cf. Hypsochromic shift

B bands (u.v.)
Under the Moser and Kohlenberg[17] nomenclature the B bands are those corresponding to the most powerful electronic transitions giving rise to strong absorptions, usually above 220 nm with molar extinction coefficients (q.v.) exceeding 5000.

see also Bands (ultraviolet)

Beer law (u.v., i.r.)
The portion of incident radiant energy absorbed by a material in solution is proportional to the concentration of that material.

Mathematically this is expressed as

$$-\frac{dI}{dc} \propto I$$

which on integration becomes

$$\log \frac{I_0}{I} = k_2 c$$

see also Beer–Lambert law; Absorbance

Beer, Bernard, Bouguer and Lambert laws
Considerable confusion exists over the prior claim and mode of reference to these individual laws and their combined form.

The fundamental law relating absorption and thickness of the medium is frequently credited to Lambert[21], although he actually restated and extended a law that had been originally enunciated by Bouguer[22]. The second fundamental law dealing with absorption and its relation to concentration was published by Beer[23] shortly prior to its publication in the same year by Bernard[24]. The whole of this very confused story has been sorted out by Malinin and Yoe[25].

Generally the combined form of the two related laws is referred to as the Beer–Lambert law (q.v.).

14

Beer–Bouguer law (i.r., u.v.)
>*see* Beer–Lambert law

Beer–Lambert law (i.r., u.v.)
The combined form of the absorption laws is obtained[26] by integrating the equation

$$dI = \left(\frac{\partial I}{\partial l}\right)_c dl + \left(\frac{\partial I}{\partial c}\right)_l dc$$

giving a mathematical expression of the form

$$\log \frac{I_0}{I} = alc$$

in which a is a constant and l and c are empirical units for sample path length and concentration respectively.

The more specific form of this equation is

$$\log \frac{I_0}{I} = \varepsilon lc$$

>*see also* Absorbance

Bending vibrations (i.r.)
For a non-linear molecule consisting of n atoms there are $3n - 6$ vibrational modes ($3n - 5$ for a linear molecule), and of these $2n - 5$ are bending (or deformation) vibrations. In these vibrations the motion occurs in a direction perpendicular to the bond between the atoms. Bending vibrations are frequently subdivided into four types rocking, scissor, twisting and wagging.

plane of atoms

rocking   scissor   twisting   wagging

plane of atoms

Figure 4. Bending vibrations

cf. Stretching vibrations

15

Bernard law

see Beer law

Binomial series

This is the series of values obtained by the expansion of the general expression $(x + y)^n$ for positive values of n.

$$(x + y)^n = x^n + nx^{n-1}y + \frac{n(n-1)}{2}x^{n-2}y^2 \ldots y^n$$

The general term ($m + 1$ term) for the expression is given by

$$\frac{n!}{m!(n-m)!} x^{n-m}y^m$$

The coefficients for the individual terms in the binomial expansion for increasing values of n correspond to the relative intensities of peaks in proton magnetic resonance multiplets arising as a result of first-order coupling. The values are best arranged in the form of the Pascal triangle (q.v.).

Black-body radiation

Emission of radiation from incandescent solids depends upon the chemical composition and physical nature of the material. A black body is both a perfect absorber of radiant energy and a perfect radiator. Any radiation striking the black body is absorbed without loss due to reflection or transmission. The main interest in black-body radiation is in the distribution of the radiation emitted when the black body is heated, and this is taken as a standard for any source used to produce radiant energy for infrared spectrometers. Thus the suitability of the Nernst glower (q.v.) and the globar (q.v.) are assessed by comparison with the energy distribution from a black body as shown in the figure below.

The total emission of radiant energy is expressed by the Stefan–Boltzmann law (q.v.) whilst the Wien laws (q.v.), the Rayleigh and Jeans law (q.v.) and the Planck law (q.v.) serve to describe other aspects of the relationship between energy, wavelength and temperature.

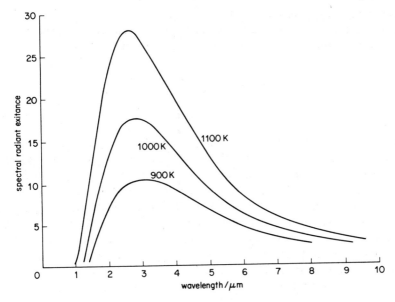

Figure 5. Distribution of black-body radiation

Bloch equations (n.m.r.)

Development of the Bloch equations[27] assisted not only the calculation of magnetic moments in magnetic fields, but also the calculation of the shapes of absorption curves for simple n.m.r. spectra to be made[28]. When referred to a set of rotating axes the equations take the following form:

$$\frac{\mathrm{d}M_x}{\mathrm{d}t} = \gamma(M_y H_0 + M_z H_1 \sin \omega_L t) - \frac{M_x}{T_2}$$

$$\frac{\mathrm{d}M_y}{\mathrm{d}t} = \gamma(M_z H_1 \cos \omega_L t - M_x H_0) - \frac{M_y}{T_2}$$

$$\frac{\mathrm{d}M_z}{\mathrm{d}t} = \gamma(-M_x H_1 \sin \omega_L t - M_y H_1 \cos \omega_L t) - \frac{M_z - H_0}{T_1}$$

Blue shift (u.v.)

see Hypsochromic shift

17

Bohr magneton μ_B (e.s.r., n.m.r.)
This is the unit of magnetic moment employed extensively in calculations of electron spin effects and electron–nuclear spin interactions.

$$\mu_B = \frac{eh}{4\pi m_e} = \frac{e\hbar}{2m_e} = 9{\cdot}274\,096 \times 10^{-24} \text{ J T}^{-1}$$

Bolometer (i.r.)
The bolometer, or thermistor, is a detector used in infrared spectrometers. Absorption of radiation by the thermistor surface leads to a temperature change with a consequent alteration in the resistance. By incorporating the thermistor as one arm of a Wheatstone bridge (q.v.) circuit a current flow is obtained proportional to the amount of energy incident on the detector[29].

The sensitive part of the thermistor is a 5 mm square flake, about 10 μm thick, made from a mixture of manganese, nickel and cobalt oxides[30]. The resistance change is about 4% for every degC rise in temperature. Highly sensitive bolometers suitable for operating at low temperatures have been made from superconductors such as columbian (niobium) nitride[31].

Boltzmann constant k
The Boltzmann constant is the ideal gas constant per molecule, the value being given by

$$k = \frac{R}{N_A} = 1{\cdot}380\,622 \times 10^{-23} \text{ J K}^{-1}$$
$$= 1{\cdot}380\,622 \times 10^{-16} \text{ g cm}^2 \text{ s}^{-2} \text{ deg}^{-1}$$

Boltzmann distribution
$\qquad\qquad$ *see* Maxwell–Boltzmann distribution

Boltzmann principle
This gives the statistical distribution of particles for any system subjected to thermal agitation under the influence of an electric, magnetic or gravitational field.

$$N_E = N\mathrm{e}^{-E/kT}$$

Boltzmann ratio
From the Boltzmann principle it can be shown that the ratio of the population in an upper energy state to that in a lower energy state is given by

$$\frac{N_E{}'}{N_E{}''} = e^{-h\nu/kT}$$

for nuclear energy levels this becomes

$$\frac{N_E{}'}{N_E{}''} = e^{-\mu H/IkT}$$

Bonding orbitals (u.v.)
When two atomic orbitals are combined to form a molecular orbital two possible types of bonding can take place. If the two electrons have opposite spins the electron cloud of the molecular orbital is mainly between the two nuclei and the orbital energy level is lower than either of the two contributing atomic orbitals. This constitutes a bonding orbital.

If, however, the two electrons have identical spins the molecular orbital is formed with a nodal plane between the two nuclei and the charge is localized at each end of the bond. This is an anti-bonding orbital and has a higher energy level than either of the contributing atomic orbitals.

The anti-bonding counterparts to sigma (σ) and pi (π) bonding orbitals are designated σ^* and π^*.

Bouguer law (i.r., u.v.)
> *see* Beer–Lambert law; Lambert law

Brackett spectral lines (em.)
> *see* Atomic spectra

Brewster angle (r.s.)
Light incident upon a transparent surface is both reflected and refracted, the degree of each being dependent upon the angle of incidence of the light. The Brewster angle is the angle at which the incident light is totally reflected if in one polarization and totally refracted if in the opposite polarization. As a result it is possible to produce a plane polarized refracted ray from a

19

light beam of mixed polarizations. Windows arranged at the Brewster angle are employed in the lasers (q.v.) used in Raman spectroscopy (q.v.). The Brewster angle can be calculated from the relationship

$$\tan \theta_{\text{Brewster}} = n \text{ of the refracting material}$$

For example, for flint glass $n = 1\cdot66$, hence the Brewster angle $= 50° 56'$.

Broad-band n.m.r.

Solids and viscous liquids give broad absorption peaks, when studied under n.m.r. conditions, that correspond to the total proton content of the material. Low-resolution broad-band n.m.r. spectroscopy has been developed for the determination of water and fat content in powders and seeds based upon this idea. The instruments for this purpose employ a large solid sample volume, 40 ml, in a 600–700 G (0·6–0·7 T) magnetic field with a r.f. of 2·7 MHz, and can determine liquid contents as low as 0·5% in the sample. The technique has been applied to the determination of H_2O in D_2O and to the liquid content in slurries[32].

Burner (a.s.)

In many flame photometers the steady flame needed for the atomic spectra is obtained by using a modified Meker burner. The fuel gas (q.v.) is passed through a small orifice and mixed with a large amount of air before being burnt above the metal grill at the top of the burner. After nebulization the sample solution is introduced directly into the flame.

For atomic absorption spectroscopy (q.v.) the burner is a long horizontal tube with a narrow slit along its length. This produces a thin flame with a long path length which can be turned into or away from the source of radiant energy.

see also Nebulizer

C

Calibration lines (em.)

see R.U.

Calibration peaks (i.r., u.v.)

To correct for any errors in spectral chart alignment and for spectral deviations due to instrumental variations it is common practice to use a standard compound to place known absorption peaks as 'markers' on the spectra of materials under examination.

An extensive list of spectral standards has been compiled for the calibration of spectra in this way[33,34]; the list includes the characteristic absorptions for elements such as neon and argon as well as simple molecules like carbon dioxide, acetylene and nitric oxide.

The most common substance employed as a marker for infrared spectra is polystyrene; strong peaks at 3027 cm^{-1} (3·30 μm), 2851 cm^{-1} (3·51 μm), 1602 cm^{-1} (6·24 μm), 1028 cm^{-1} (9·73 μm) and 907 cm^{-1} (11·03 μm) being of particular use for this purpose. Ammonia and indene have also been used.

calibration peak	1	2	3	4	5
wavenumber (vacuum)/cm^{-1}	3027	2851	1602	1028	907

Figure 6. Calibration peak spectrum of polystyrene

Carbon filament atom reservoir (a.s.)

The study of atomic absorption and atomic fluorescence spectra has been advanced by the development of carbon filament and carbon tube atom reservoirs. These enable materials to be examined without the use of highly inflammable materials and obviate the use of nebulizer (q.v.) sampling systems.

The sample (2–50 μl) is deposited in the centre of a graphite filament and evaporated by passing a current through the graphite. It is then atomized, in an inert atmosphere, at 2500 °C by passing a large current (20–500 A) through the graphite. Signals produced by this method can last for several seconds[35].

Graphite rods and tubes may be used hundreds of times. By their use flameless atomic absorption has increased sensitivities by several orders of magnitude and is frequently superior to neutron activation analysis[36].

Figure 7. Graphite rod sampling system

see also Delves cup; Massmann furnace; Tantalum boat

Cartesian coordinates
Any point or object in three dimensions can be located fully by reference to three axes, the Cartesian coordinates, mutually perpendicular to each other, usually denoted as x, y and z axes. They are named after the mathematician Descartes.

Cascade process (a.s., u.v.)
The term given to the procedure for increasing the strength of a weak signal by the progressive build-up of electron displacement in a series of dynode plates (q.v.) in a photomultiplier (q.v.).

C.A.T. (n.m.r.)
see Computer of average transients

Cathode
The negative electrode in an electron tube or electron bombardment ion source (q.v.), it acts as an emitter of electrons and as a collector for positively charged particles. In a mass spectrometer it is the source of electrons for the ionization and fragmentation processes. In this case the accelerating slits (q.v.) must be negative with respect to the cathode in order to attract the positive ions into the analyser tube (q.v.).

Cauchy distribution
see Lorentzian curve

Cavity cell (e.s.r.)
The absorption cell most commonly employed in electron spin resonance studies is a resonant cavity formed by closing off the ends of a short length of waveguide (q.v.) cut to a simple multiple of the wavelength dimension of the guide. This leads to the microwave power being concentrated in the cavity by reflection between the ends. The sample is contained in a quartz tube inserted into the centre of the cavity.

Cavity cell (i.r.)
see Microcells

C bands (u.v.)
Moser and Kohlenberg[17] designated the absorption bands occurring on the longer-wavelength side of the main absorption band for conjugated systems as the C bands.
see Bands (ultraviolet)

23

Centre of symmetry (i.r.)

A molecule possesses a centre of symmetry when a line drawn from any atom and passing through the centre of the molecule meets an identical atom in a corresponding position diametrically opposite.

see also Axis of symmetry; Plane of symmetry

c.g.s. units

A system of units based upon the centimetre, gramme and second now obsolescent and superseded by SI units (q.v.).

Charge on an electron

see Electron

Chemical actinometer (pl.)

Rates of photochemical reactions are studied by the use of this special type of detector system. Essentially it is a cell containing a chemical compound which undergoes a reaction on exposure to light. The extent of the reaction is a measure of the quantity of radiation to which it has been subjected. One substance used for this purpose, covering the wavelength range 250–500 nm is potassium trisoxalato-ferrate(III) trihydrate, $K_3Fe(C_2O_4)_3$. $3H_2O$, in sulphuric acid[37]. The photochemical reaction produces iron(II) ions which are measured quantitatively as the 1,10-phenanthroline complex. This can detect $5 \times 10^{-10}N$ quanta and is accurate to $\pm 2\%$.

Chemical actinometers have also been developed in the form of transparent films[38] incorporating o-nitrobenzaldehyde. This system is useful for studying radiation intensities between 300 and 410 nm.

Chemical shift (n.m.r.)

In an n.m.r. spectrum the chemical shift is the displacement between the absorption peak of the nucleus of interest and the absorption peak of an appropriate reference standard. In proton studies the sharp absorption band of the methyl groups of tetramethylsilane (*see* TMS), included as an internal standard, is the reference peak against which the chemical shifts of other peaks are measured. For phosphorus nuclei the reference is normally phosphoric acid.

In quantitative terms the difference may be measured in hertz (q.v.), or in δ or τ parts per million (q.v.)[39]. As the chemical shift is proportional to the field strength, comparison of values obtained on different instruments is best achieved by using the dimensionless units of parts per million. τ values are specifically referred to TMS in proton spectra.

Chemical shift values obtained for different protons are dependent upon the individual chemical and magnetic environments; in general a high electron density around the protons leads to a small chemical shift and vice versa.

see also Deshielding; Shielding

Chemical shift reagents (n.m.r.)

Since the original observation of the effect on cholesterol[40] a number of paramagnetic lanthanide complexes have been found in which the central lanthanide ion can increase its coordination number by interaction with lone pair electrons (q.v.) in functional groups of organic compounds. The result of this is that the n.m.r. spectrum of an organic compound can be altered and significant changes in chemical shifts (q.v.) may be observed. The method can be used to obtain greater information about the molecular structure, particularly in cases in which the normal n.m.r. spectrum possesses overlapping absorption signals[41].

First-order spectra have been obtained by the use of tris-(dipivalo-methanato) europium, $Eu(DPM)_3$, whilst other work[42] has shown that tris-(2, 2, 6, 6-tetramethylheptane-3, 5-dionato)-praseodymium, $Pr(tmhd)_3$, is of similar value for both ^1H and ^{13}C n.m.r. spectra.

Chemiluminescence (pl.)

Luminescence (q.v.) occurring during the course of chemical reactions is termed chemiluminescence. It arises from the emission of radiation from molecules that have absorbed energy during the course of the chemical reaction.

Chopper

see Rotating sector mirror

Chromatic aberration

As the refractive index for any transparent substance differs for the different wavelengths of the light the individual wavelengths are dispersed by varying amounts. As a result white light can be dispersed into its individual wavelengths including the infrared, ultraviolet and visible spectra (q.v.). Images produced by lenses will, therefore, possess coloured edges due to the chromatic aberration of the lens.

see also Dispersion

Chromophore (u.v.)

Chemical functional groups which are capable of exhibiting characteristic absorptions in the ultraviolet and visible regions of the spectrum even when they are not in conjugation with or affected by the influence of other groups are called chromophores. Most chromophores possess some degree of unsaturation, the carbonyl group being typical and exhibiting absorptions between 160 and 170 nm and between 180 and 190 nm.

Chromophoric absorption values are greatly enhanced when conjugation exists between chromophores or when they are influenced by auxochromes (q.v.).

see also Hyperchromic effect

Circular dichroism

Optically active materials frequently absorb left and right circularly polarized light to different extents. The value for the circular dichroism at a particular wavelength is $\varepsilon_1 - \varepsilon_r$. This varies with the change in wavelength and the relationship

$$\Delta\varepsilon = f(\lambda)$$

gives a bell-shaped curve, with $\Delta\varepsilon$ possessing either positive or negative values.

Collimator

This part of the optical system of a photometer is a lens or mirror arranged to produce a parallel beam of light to or from the prism or diffraction grating. For this purpose the radiation source is placed at the focal point of a divergent lens; alternatively this can be achieved by passing the radiation through a narrow slit at the focal point of the lens.

Combination lines (n.m.r.)

Combination lines occur when two or more nuclei undergo simultaneous changes of spin states (q.v.), giving rise to overlapping peaks in the n.m.r. spectrum. First-order spectra (q.v.) do not usually have peaks due to combination transitions although these can appear under saturation conditions.

Combination modes or vibrations (i.r.)

A number of weak absorptions occur in infrared spectra corresponding to the sum of two or more fundamental vibrational frequencies. These combination modes arise from the anharmonicities of the oscillators which leads to an interaction of the vibrational states in polyatomic molecules. The resulting absorptions are weak compared with those due to fundamental vibrations and overtones (q.v.).

cf. Difference modes

Computer of average transients (n.m.r.)

The C.A.T. is a device employed in n.m.r. spectrometers to increase the size of weak signals compared with the general noise level. Spectra are repeatedly recorded and stored in the memory of a small computer. For 'n' scans the increase of the signal size over the noise is $\sqrt{n}$. This is because for n scans the signal increases n times while the noise, which is random, increases $\sqrt{n}$ times and the nett improvement is $n/\sqrt{n}$ or $\sqrt{n}$. Thus a spectrum scanned forty-nine times gives a seven-fold improvement over a single scan.

The technique is currently more common than is Fourier-transform n.m.r. (q.v.) which can also be used to obtain improved spectra.

Contact hyperfine interaction (e.s.r.)

see Fermi contact interaction

Continuous laser (r.s.)

see Laser

Continuous mode (m.s.)

A method for the continuous production of positive ions in the time-of-flight mass spectrometer (q.v.). Ionization and fragmentation of molecules is carried out by a continuous stream of electrons throughout the cycle of operations in order to produce a constant supply of positive ions. The ions are only attracted away during the drawout pulse of the instrument.

cf. Pulsed mode

Continuous spectra (em.)

Incandescent solids emit continuous spectra over a broad band usually with the absence of any sharply defined lines. Materials producing such spectra include ceramics and fused silicacious mixtures. In some cases the broad emission of radiation approximates to that from a black body (q.v.) and such substances can be used as radiation sources for infrared spectroscopy.

see also Globar; Nernst glower; Opperman source

Contour (n.m.r.)

see Curvature

Cornu mounting

The Cornu mounting is the prism system employed in those spectrophotometers in which radiation is passed in through one face of the prism and out through the opposite face. The prism employed for this purpose is formed from two 30° quartz prisms, one of right-handed quartz and the other of left-handed quartz, joined to give a 60° prism producing admirable dispersion but no polarization.

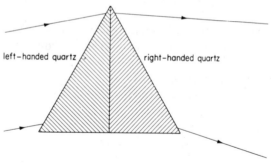

Figure 8. Cornu prism

Coupling constant a_H (e.s.r.)

Hyperfine splitting in electron spin resonance spectra occurs as a result of the interaction of atomic nuclei with the electrons of the system under examination. The coupling constant is the distance between the individual peaks in the hyperfine splitting multiplet; its value is determined by the

28

extent of coupling arising from the magnetic moments of the interacting nuclei and is expressed in gauss.

Coupling constant *J* (n.m.r.)
The coupling constant (measured in hertz) is the separation between the peaks of a first-order multiplet produced as a result of spin–spin coupling (q.v.). The larger the value of *J*, the greater is the coupling between the nuclei. The value of *J* is independent of the operating frequency of the instrument upon which it is measured.

Cracking pattern (m.s.)
Another name for the characteristic fragmentation spectrum obtained for a substance by mass spectrometry.
see Mass spectrum

Crossed-coil method (n.m.r.)
see Induction method

Crystal detector (e.s.r.)
In electron spin resonance spectrometers a silicon–tungsten crystal rectifier is usually employed as the detector. This is located at the end of one arm of the hybrid T (q.v.) and receives a signal only when absorption of energy occurs in the sample cavity. The crystal produces a direct current proportional to the square root of the microwave signal.

Curvature (n.m.r.)
A synonym for the contour of the magnetic field strength of a magnet between the pole pieces. The contour may be spoken of as 'dome-shaped', 'dish-shaped' or 'flat'. Absorption peaks will be distorted unless the contour is flat. The curvature of the field is adjusted during the tuning up procedure and is carried out roughly by cycling (q.v.) the electromagnet.

Cuvette
Another name given to the glass or silica sample tubes used for the study of liquids and solutions in ultraviolet and fluorescent spectroscopy.

Cycles per second (n.m.r.)

Cycles per second (n.m.r.)

see Hertz

Cycling (n.m.r.)

A rough adjustment of the curvature (q.v.) of the magnetic field strength between the pole pieces of an electromagnet is obtained by passing an abnormally large current through the coils of the electromagnet for two or three minutes followed by a reduction to the normal operating current level for the instrument. The operation is intended to produce a flatter contour of the magnetic field strength between the poles.

see also Shim coils

Czerny–Turner mounting

By using two concave mirrors with a plane diffraction grating a stigmatic (q.v.) and achromatic (q.v.) optical system is produced. By this means all wavelengths are brought to a focus without changing the detector to mirror distance in the spectrometer. Any change in wavelength is simply obtained by rotating the grating. This type of system[43,44] is a modification of that described by Ebert[45] in 1889. The Czerny–Turner mounting is now used for monochromation in a wide range of spectrometers including those for emission and Raman spectroscopy.

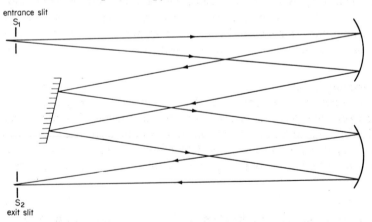

entrance slit
S_1

S_2
exit slit

Figure 9. Czerny–Turner mounting

D

Dark current
This is the background current that flows in photoemissive and photo-conductive detectors, such as those used in ultraviolet and infrared spectro-photometers, when no radiant energy is falling upon the detector. It is a temperature-dependent effect and in manual single-beam instruments must be corrected for before taking a reading on every occasion. Operation of these detectors at low temperatures (-20 °C) reduces the dark current by many orders of magnitude compared with that at room temperature.

Daughter ion (m.s.)
In a transition involving metastable ions (q.v.) the daughter ion is the actual ion recorded by the detector, although its mass/charge value is recorded as the value M^* instead of the correct M_B.

D bands (u.v.)
Within the ultraviolet region the weakest absorption band for conjugated compounds occurs at the longest wavelengths. Moser and Kohlenberg[17] designated these as the D bands.
                    see Bands (ultraviolet)

d.c. arc source (em.)
Samples can be vaporized for emission spectroscopy by subjecting them to a d.c. arc produced by a voltage of up to 300 V, and leads to electronic transitions in elements. The temperature within the arc may be as high as 8000 K. In most instruments the arc is struck between graphite electrodes. The d.c. arc is particularly useful for the study of neutral atoms present in small amounts.
                    see also a.c. arc source; a.c. spark source

Decoupling (n.m.r.)
                    see Multiple resonance

Deformation vibrations (i.r.)
                    see Bending vibrations

31

Degeneracy
This term is used when one energy level corresponds to two or more states of motion. It arises when the symmetry of a molecule is such that certain fundamental frequencies are equal and is a common feature in infrared spectroscopy. When two such frequencies are equal the system is termed doubly degenerate and when three frequencies are equal it is triply degenerate.

Degrees of freedom (i.r., r.s.)
For a molecule of n atoms there exist a total of $3n$ degrees of freedom. In the case of a non-linear molecule there are three translational degrees of freedom and three rotational degrees of freedom leaving a total of $3n - 6$ vibrational degrees of freedom. For a linear molecule the number of vibrational degrees of freedom is $3n-5$. Vibrational degrees of freedom may be further subdivided into bending vibrations (q.v.) and stretching vibrations (q.v.).

Delta values (n.m.r.)
        see Parts per million; Chemical shift

Delves cup (a.s.)
Very rapid determinations of the lead content of blood samples are obtained by introducing the sample contained in a small nickel cup[46] directly into the non-luminous air–acetylene flame of an atomic absorption spectrometer. The blood samples are partially oxidized by hydrogen peroxide before the analysis which takes about five minutes from beginning to end, the actual atomic absorption reading only requiring·a few seconds.

Densitometer comparator (em.)
In both qualitative and quantitative emission spectroscopy the nature of unknown substances is determined by comparison with a series of standard spectra. This is done using special comparators in which two plates can be studied side by side. In the most modern forms of instrument the two plates are illuminated, and enlarged images projected onto a screen as illustrated below.

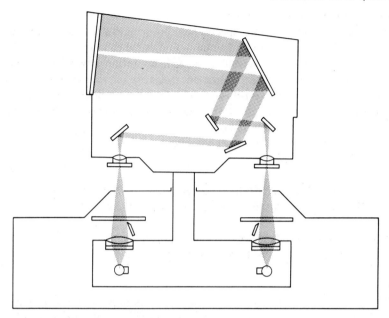

Figure 10. Optical arrangement of a projection comparator

Depolarization factor (or ratio) ρ_N (r.s.)
By enclosing the sample tube in polarizing sheets each line in a Raman spectrum can be split into a horizontal component (I_h) and a vertical component (I_v). The depolarization factor (ρ_N) is the ratio of these two components. As I_v is always weaker than I_h the value of ρ_N is less than unity. The theoretical limit for the value of ρ_N is 0·857.

$$\rho_N = \frac{I_v}{I_h}$$

Derivative curve (e.s.r.)
The derivative curve for any distribution is obtained by differentiating the equation for the particular distribution. Electron spin resonance spectra (q.v.) are normally recorded as the derivative curves obtained by applying a modulating field to the absorption current. The shapes of these curves are obtained by differentiating the Gaussian (normal) distribution (q.v.).

33

Deshielding (n.m.r.)

Absorption peaks on n.m.r. spectra that occur at low field strength (away from the TMS signal) are said to be deshielded if they absorb at low field on the n.m.r. spectrum as a result of being in a position in which the induced magnetic field produced by the electron circulation acts in the same direction as the applied field. Protons in the $-CHO$ group of aldehydes are typical of deshielded atoms as a result of the electron circulation of the electrons forming the carbonyl double bond.

see also Ring current effect; Shielding

Detectors

see Barrier layer cell; Bolometer; Photoelectric detector; Photomultiplier; Photoemissive tube; Pneumatic cell; Thermocouple

Deuterium discharge lamp (u.v.)

see Hydrogen discharge lamp

Deuterium exchange (n.m.r.)

The presence of exchangeable protons, such as those attached to oxygen and nitrogen, can be shown in n.m.r. spectra by their disappearance from the spectrum after the sample has been shaken with D_2O. This has the advantage that in cases in which the absorptions of the exchangeable protons overlap with those of other protons the spectrum may be substantially simplified by deuterium exchange. The resulting peak for the HDO molecules formed (arising near to 5δ) can be used to estimate the number of exchangeable protons in the molecule.

Diamagnetic anisotropy (n.m.r.)

Shielding and deshielding (q.v.) of protons are dependent upon the orientation of the protons with respect to any induced magnetic fields and are known collectively as anisotropic effects. Diamagnetic anisotropy is brought about by the circulation of electrons within π and σ electron clouds and leads to deshielding in the case of aldehydic protons, but shielding in the case of acetylenic protons.

Diamagnetic shielding (screening) (n.m.r.)

see Shielding

Diamagnetism
This is the magnetic property possessed by a material as a result of the circulation of electrons. The magnetism produced acts in opposition to that of the applied field. Where unpaired electrons exist in a substance paramagnetism (q.v.) arises and this is dominant over any diamagnetism.

Difference modes (i.r.)
Some of the absorptions recorded in infrared spectra correspond to the difference between two vibrational frequencies. In these cases the molecule already existing in one excited vibrational state absorbs enough additional radiant energy to raise it to another vibrational level in a different vibrational mode. The measured absorption is then the difference between the two.
cf. Combination modes

Diffraction
Diffraction occurs when a wavefront passes through narrow slits and holes and at sharp edges. In the case of a number of parallel slits the effect is to produce a series of wavefronts which are refracted away from the original line of direction. This idea is the basis of the diffraction grating (q.v.) used extensively in spectrophotometers, although most instruments now use the echelette reflectance gratings.

Diffraction gratings
see Gratings

α, α-diphenyl-β-picrylhydrazyl (e.s.r.)
see DPPH

Dipole–dipole broadening (n.m.r.)
A broadening of n.m.r. absorption peaks occurs both in the solid state and in viscous liquids as a result of the magnetic dipoles because the magnetic field strength varies throughout such media. This variation arises because the physical nature of the material prevents the averaging out of the magnetic fields due to the nuclei.

35

Direct inlet system (m.s.)

Substances possessing low vapour pressures can be introduced into a mass spectrometer, in the absence of a probe inlet device, by bleeding directly from the sample holder into the ionization chamber without using an intermediate reservoir expansion chamber or leak valve. The system is unsuitable for any substance possessing a high volatility.

see also Batch inlet system; Direct insertion probe

Direct insertion probe (m.s.)

Solids and involatile liquid samples can be vaporized into the ionization chamber of the mass spectrometer by placing them in a small glass sample tube on the end of a rod that can be inserted into the instrument, through a vacuum lock, to a position close to the ionizing beam. Direct insertion probes can be heated up to 350 °C by means of a filament around the sample holder, and some can also be operated at temperatures as low as -50 °C by passing liquid N_2 through the probe.

Figure 11. Direct insertion probe

see also Batch inlet system; Direct inlet system

Dispersion

In its loosest sense this expression is employed to describe the ability of any transparent substance to separate the wavelengths of radiant energy passing through. In spectroscopy it is used with special reference to the prisms (q.v.) and gratings (q.v.) employed for the monochromation of ultraviolet, visible and infrared radiation.

For very small slit widths dispersion depends only on the refractive index of the material and the size of the prism. The dispersive power for a prism is given by $\partial n/\partial\lambda$ and is used in the calculation of the resolution (q.v.).

For gratings the dispersion is given by $\partial\theta/\partial\lambda = n/a\cos\theta$ where a is the distance between adjacent lines, θ the angle of reflectance and n the order of the spectrum. If θ is small $\cos\theta \approx 1$ and $\partial\theta/\partial\lambda = n/a$.

see also Gratings; Prisms

Doppler broadening (a.s., em.)
One of the causes of the broadening of absorption and emission spectral lines is the thermal motion of the atoms. Doppler broadening is the name given to this effect and is proportional to $(T/A_r)^{1/2}$.

cf. Pressure broadening

Doppler effect
The apparent change in frequency of a wave motion passing through a stationary medium, as determined by the detector, as a result of the relative movement of the source towards or away from the detector is known as the Doppler effect. In spectroscopy any moving source will give rise to a Doppler shift and this is one of the features of Mössbauer spectroscopy (q.v.). The shift has also been detected in the spectra of moving stars.

Line broadening in the spectra of gases occurs because of the different speeds of the individual gas molecules giving rise to the Doppler effect.

Double-coil method (n.m.r.)
see Induction method

Double-focusing mass spectrometer (m.s.)
This instrument analyses the positive beam using both a radial electrostatic analyser and a magnetic field analyser. The electrostatic analyser acts as an energy selector and improves the focusing compared with the simple magnetic deflection mass spectrometer (q.v.). As a result resolution (q.v.) of up to 10 000 can be obtained.

Figure 12. Double-focusing mass spectrometer

Double irradiation (n.m.r.)
> *see* Multiple resonance

Double monochromator (i.r., r.s.)
The system of double monochromation employs both a prism and a grating and is used in better quality spectrophotometers. The purpose of the prism is to remove the unwanted higher orders of diffraction produced by the grating (q.v.).

An alternative, but poorer, method of double monochromation uses two prisms, the exit slit of the first monochromator serving as the entrance slit for the second.

Double monochromation gives improved resolution but there is some loss of energy due to increased path length and absorption. Present Raman spectrophotometers use a double monochromator formed from two diffraction gratings.

Double resonance (n.m.r.)
> *see* INDOR; Multiple resonance

Doubly charged ions (m.s.)
Some of the positively charged ionic species detected in mass spectrometry are found to carry a double charge (and sometimes even more). These give rise to mass/charge peaks at half the true mass value for the ions, as in these cases the instrument is detecting $m/2e$. For ions possessing an odd true mass value the peak for the doubly charged ion is found as having an apparent half mass unit falling between two integral mass/charge values.

DPPH (e.s.r.)
This is the common standard used for comparison in electron spin resonance studies as it exists completely in the free radical state. It contains 1.63×10^{21} unpaired electrons per gramme and can be diluted to give an e.s.r. signal corresponding to any required number of electrons by using carbon black as a diluent. It can also be used as a solution in benzene.

α, α-diphenyl-β-picrylhydrazyl

Drift region (m.s.)
In time-of-flight mass spectrometers (q.v.) the charged ions pass along a straight tube about two metres long. This is the drift region of the instrument and the period of time spent by the ions in the tube increases with the mass of the ion.

DSS (n.m.r.)
Sodium-2,2-dimethyl-2-silapentane-5-sulphonate, $(CH_3)_3SiCH_2CH_2CH_2$-SO_3Na is an alternative reference to TMS for proton n.m.r. Its main advantage is that it is a water-soluble solid and can be used as an internal standard (q.v.) in aqueous and D_2O solutions, with which TMS is immiscible.

39

Dynamic nuclear polarization (n.m.r.)
see Overhauser effect

Dynode
This is an electron-sensitive plate used in photomultipliers (q.v.). Amplification of signals is achieved by directing photoelectrons onto the dynode plate which is designed to give a multiplication factor of at least two for every primary electron falling on it. The plate is most commonly made from a copper–beryllium or silver–magnesium alloy. A series of dynodes is employed in photomultiplier tubes to produce a cascade process (q.v.).

E

E bands (u.v.)
Bowden and Braude[14] assigned the letter E to the weak ultraviolet absorptions arising from the movement of electrons in aromatic systems. These are only measured in the vacuum u.v. region below 200 nm. This system of nomenclature conflicts with that used by other authors.
see Bands (ultraviolet)

Echelette gratings
see Gratings

Effective bandwidth (i.r., u.v.)
No monochromator produces a completely isolated single wavelength from a polychromatic source, but actually gives a spread on either side of the required value. Comparisons between monochromators can be made on the basis of the effective bandwidth as this is the width of the transmittance band at half the maximum transmittance value. The narrower the effective bandwidth the greater is the degree of monochromation. For work in the ultraviolet region the effective bandwidth needs to be < 1 nm. The diagram below shows the inter-relationship between the effective bandwidth, the required monochromatic wavelength and the maximum per cent transmittance for the monochromator.

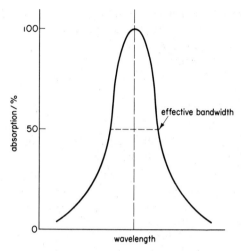

Figure 13. Effective bandwidth

Eigenfunction Ψ

This is a position-dependent amplitude and when multiplied by its complex conjugate Ψ^* it gives the probability

$$P = \Psi^*\Psi$$

that a given particle occupies a particular defined position. An eigenfunction must be an acceptable solution of the wave equation.

see Schrödinger wave equation

Eigenvalues

These are values obtained from solving the Schrödinger wave equation (q.v.) for eigenfunctions of a system.

Einstein E

The einstein is the amount of energy absorbed by one mole of material undergoing a photochemical reaction and is based upon the Stark Einstein law (q.v.).

$$E = N_A h\nu$$

Electrical discharge getter pumps (m.s.)
    see Sputter-ion pump

Electric quadrupole broadening (n.m.r.)
    see Quadrupole broadening

Electrodeless discharge tubes (a.s.)
These sources for atomic absorption and atomic fluorescence were originally developed for alkali metal determinations. Radiation intensities obtained are much greater than those from the corresponding hollow cathode lamps (q.v.) and produce very sharp spectral lines[49].

They consist of a quartz tube 2–7 cm long and 8 mm in internal diameter containing up to 20 mg of the required element (identical with that to be studied) and sometimes an equal amount of iodine. The tubes are filled with argon at low pressure (about 2 torr)[50]. Under the operating conditions all the charge in the tube should be in the vapour state. The tubes are subjected to a microwave frequency of 2000 to 3000 MHz.

Electrodes (em.)
For most emission spectrometry using arc and spark procedures the samples are placed in a small curved recess in the end of a graphite electrode. The second, upper, electrode is a similar graphite rod shaped to a point and aligned with the sample.

In some cases, where the sample is a solid conductor, the electrodes may be made from the sample itself. Metallic electrodes have been used for general determinations but are best employed for providing reference spectra of themselves.

A special type of electrode that can be reused one hundred times has been developed[47] from vitreous carbon, and is called the glassy electrode. It is claimed to give emission spectra three times as intense as those obtained from graphite electrodes and is less prone to contamination owing to its pore-free surface[48]. The glassy electrode enables metals in solution to be determined with a greater precision.

Electromagnetic spectrum
For most spectroscopic purposes the electromagnetic spectrum is considered to consist of the region of radiant energy ranging from wavelengths

of 10 metres to 1×10^{-10} centimetres. Only certain portions of this range are currently used for spectroscopic measurements, although many wavelengths are used for such purposes as broadcasting and radar. The diagram below illustrates the scope of the present applications.

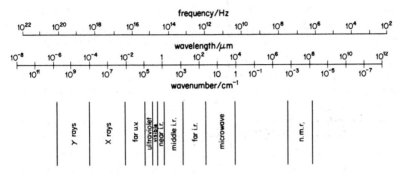

Figure 14. The electromagnetic spectrum

Electron
This name is most commonly used for the negatively charged elementary particle more specifically called the negatron. The mass (at rest) is $m_e = 9{\cdot}109\ 558 \times 10^{-31}$ kg with a charge of $1{\cdot}602\ 191\ 7 \times 10^{-19}$ C, and a spin quantum number of $\frac{1}{2}$.

The positive electron, possessing identical values but an opposite charge, is called the positron.

Electron bombardment ion source (m.s.)
The formation of positive ions by electron bombardment of molecules is the most common form of ion source used in mass spectrometry. The molecules are passed into the ionization chamber of the spectrometer which is at a temperature of about 200 °C and a pressure of about 10^{-7} torr, where they are bombarded at right angles to their line of direction by a beam of low-energy electrons. The electrons for the bombardment are produced from an incandescent tungsten filament heated to 2000 °C with energies covering the range 10–100 eV.

To achieve adequate ionization and fragmentation for most general purposes the ionization is carried out with electrons possessing an energy

43

of 70 eV[51]. Operation at very low energy, e.g. about 20 eV, produces spectra showing little more than the parent peak (q.v.) and the base peak (q.v.).

Electronic spectra (a.s., em., u.v.)

The promotion of an electron from a lower energy state to a higher energy state is brought about by the absorption of energy by the atomic or molecular species. This energy may be measured in the form of atomic absorption spectra (q.v.) or as an ultraviolet/visible spectrum (q.v.). Where an electron drops from a higher energy state to a lower energy state there is a loss of energy from the species which may be measured in the form of an emission spectrum (q.v.).

The emission spectra from atoms occur as a series of discrete lines corresponding to fixed wavelengths (*see* Atomic spectra), but the absorption spectra for molecules are normally broad bands as the electronic transitions are accompanied by vibrational and rotational transitions (*see* Bands (ultraviolet); Ultraviolet/visible spectrum).

The energy differences between electronic levels vary from < 50 kcal mole^{-1} in visible spectra to > 300 kcal mole^{-1} in the far ultraviolet.

Electron impact induced reactions (m.s.)

This is a term used to refer to the rearrangement of fragment ions (q.v.) produced as a result of electron bombardment of molecules in mass spectrometers.

see also McLafferty rearrangement

Electron multiplier

see Photomultiplier

Electron nuclear double resonance (e.s.r.)

see ENDOR

Electron paramagnetic resonance

see Electron spin resonance

Electron spin resonance

Also known as electron paramagnetic resonance, this is the study of atoms, ions, free radicals and molecules possessing an odd number of electrons or unpaired electrons which display characteristic magnetic properties[52]. These arise from the spin properties of the unpaired electrons. Under the influence of a magnetic field the magnetic moment of the spinning electron may occupy either of two possible orientations, aligned or opposed to the magnetic field, corresponding to the two energy levels for the electron spin. The energy levels have a difference of

$$\Delta E = h\nu = g\mu_{\mathrm{B}}H$$

At resonance the absorption of energy causes the magnetic moment of the spinning electron to rise (flip) from the lower to the higher energy state.

The e.s.r. spectra are complicated by the fact that coupling occurs between the spinning electron and adjacent spinning nuclei, so that the absorption spectrum (usually recorded as a derivative curve (q.v.)), consists of a multiplicity determined by the number, nature and position of coupling nuclei. It is this feature of the spectra that makes them of value in structural elucidation.

Modern e.s.r. spectrometers can detect free radicals at concentrations as low as 10^{-13} mole. In a field of about 3400 gauss the frequency required for resonance is $9 \cdot 5 \times 10^9$ Hz.

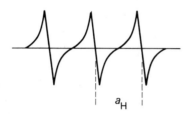

Figure 15. Splitting of an e.s.r. signal by interaction between an unpaired electron and an atomic nucleus possessing a spin quantum number $I = 1$. The measurement a_{H} is the coupling constant (q.v.)

Electronvolt eV

The electronvolt is a unit of energy traditionally associated with the motion of atomic and molecular particles. It is not a recommended SI unit (q.v.) and its use is to be progressively discouraged. The conversion factor for the unit is

$$1 \text{ eV} \approx 1 \cdot 6022 \times 10^{-19} \text{ J}$$

Emission spectra (em.)

Electrons in the ground state may be promoted to higher energy levels by excitation of the atoms using electrical or thermal means. On reverting to the ground state, or any intermediate energy level, the absorbed energy is released and may be measured and recorded to give a representation of the emission spectrum for the substance.

Three forms of emission spectra exist: these are continuous spectra (q.v.) as produced by incandescent solids, band spectra (q.v.) as given by molecules, and line spectra (q.v.) obtained from atoms.

The most widely used form of emission spectroscopy is that used for atomic spectra in which characteristic lines for metals are recorded on a photographic plate. These are particularly useful for studying the composition of alloys for purity and minor constituents. A typical emission spectrum is illustrated below; the individual peaks representing transitions between energy levels similar to those obtained with hydrogen as previously mentioned in atomic spectra (q.v.).

Figure 16. Mercury emission spectrum

ENDOR (e.s.r.)
Improved resolution of e.s.r. spectra is obtained by the electron nuclear double resonance (ENDOR) technique in which the e.s.r. line is broadened and hyperfine details enhanced[53]. This is achieved by irradiating the sample with nuclear resonance frequencies while observing the e.s.r. absorption signal.

cf. Overhauser effect

Energy levels
The total energy of an atom consists of the sum of the energies of its constituent sub-atomic particles. Each of these may exist in one of a number of energy states, and energy is absorbed or emitted by atoms as a result of transitions between the energy levels representing these states.

Transitions between electron energy levels in atoms give rise to atomic spectra (q.v.) whilst similar transitions in the energy levels of bonding electrons in molecules produce molecular spectra (q.v.) studied in the ultraviolet and visible regions.

Transitions between nuclear spin energy levels give rise to nuclear magnetic resonance spectra (q.v.).

A diagrammatic representation of the transitions between energy levels is shown when considering the Franck–Condon principle (q.v.).

Enrichers (m.s.)
To obtain a suitable concentration of sample from a gas chromatograph which can be led directly into a mass spectrometer it is necessary to separate the sample from the hydrogen or helium carrier gas. For this purpose several different forms of interface (q.v.) between the gas chromatograph and mass spectrometer have been tried as enrichers for this purpose.

see also Watson–Biemann separator

EPA mixed solvent (pl.)
Studies of phosphorescence carried out in a solid matrix at low temperatures necessitate the use of a clear medium. The EPA mixed solvent is particularly suitable for this purpose, consisting of diethyl ether, 2-methylbutane and ethanol in the ratio 5:5:2 by volume. It solidifies to a clear glass when frozen in liquid nitrogen.

see also Shpol'skii effect

e.s.r.
see Electron spin resonance

Excimer (pl.)
The term excimer (from excited dimer) was originally introduced for what were believed to be long-lived species exhibiting fluorescence after an excited molecule had reacted with a second molecule[54]. Other explanations have been found for the phenomena in this classification[55] and the word 'excimer' is now used for short-lived excited dimers of the type obtained with pyrene in which the dimer fluorescence spectrum becomes more pronounced with increased concentration of the fluorescer in solution.

Excited state
An atom in which one or more electrons have been promoted from the lowest energy level to higher energy levels is said to be in an excited state. More generally the expression is used to refer to the energy state of any molecule, atom or sub-atomic particle above that of the highest occupied energy level in the ground state.
cf. Ground state

External reference (n.m.r.)
The reference standard in n.m.r. may be contained in a capillary tube within the n.m.r. sample tube. In this form it constitutes an external standard and because of the glass walls of the capillary tube does not experience exactly the same magnetic effects as does the sample under study. This can lead to slight differences in values for chemical shifts (q.v.) compared with results using internal references (q.v.). As the normal reference material TMS (q.v.) is insoluble in solutions made up in D_2O it is common to employ external references, although an alternative to this problem is to use the water-soluble secondary standard DSS (q.v.).

Extinction coefficient E (u.v.)
This term has traditionally been used for the absorbance obtained for a 1 % solution of material in a cell of 1 cm path length and is normally used for substances of unknown molecular weight. In this case it is written in the

form $E_{1\,cm}^{1\%}$. The relationship between this and the molar extinction coefficient (q.v.) is given by

$$E_{1\,cm}^{1\%} = \frac{10\varepsilon}{\text{molecular weight}}$$

It has been suggested that the word 'absorptivity' should be used in place of extinction coefficient, but this has not met with general acceptance. Currently the recommendation is that the expression employed internationally should be 'absorption coefficient' using the symbol a such that

$$a = \frac{A}{l}$$

F

Faraday cup (m.s.)
This is the simplest form of electrical detector consisting of a metal cylinder closed at one end which serves as the collecting electrode. The ion beam travels along the axis of the cylinder and impinges at a point on the bottom producing a small d.c. voltage which is fed to an amplifier and recorder. This type of detector has been of particular value in isotopic abundance studies in mass spectrometry although it is not as sensitive as a photo-multiplier (q.v.). In most mass spectrometers the Faraday cup assembly is fitted with other electrodes which serve as ion suppressors to remove scattered ions.

Far-infrared region (i.r.)
see Infrared spectra

Fermi contact interaction (e.s.r.)
All s electrons and those in hybrid orbitals have a probability of being at the centre of an atom and in such a position would be subject to a different magnetic force from that experienced further from the centre. As it approaches the nucleus the electron acquires a large kinetic energy and its

49

velocity approaches that of light. Calculations for this state of affairs were carried out by Fermi and it has become known as the Fermi contact interaction.

This interaction involves coupling between the nuclear and electron magnetic moments and leads to differences in the hyperfine splitting of the e.s.r. signal from unpaired electrons in σ molecular orbitals and those possessing some σ character.

Fermi resonance (i.r.)

This is the term given to accidental degeneracy (q.v.) arising in polyatomic molecules in which two different vibrational states accidentally possess approximately the same energy and interact with each other. The result of this resonance is that any difference between the vibrational levels is increased. It is particularly common between a fundamental band and an overtone or combination band.

Féry glass prism (u.v.)

Use of a collimating mirror in monochromators can be obviated by using this back reflecting prism with curved faces one of which is coated with an aluminium film to serve as a reflecting surface[56]. The prism was developed for use in the Féry spectrograph in which it acts as collimator and objective in addition to carrying out dispersion[57].

Field-free region (m.s.)

In magnetic deflection mass spectrometers employing a magnetic analyser of less than 180° there is a small region in which the positive ions are not acted upon by the magnetic field. This is a section between the accelerating slits (q.v.) and the magnetic field; it is known as the field-free region and arises owing to the geometry of the instrument. In 180° magnetic analyser instruments it is avoided by placing the source and accelerator slits within the complete magnetic field.

In double-focusing mass spectrometers (q.v.) a second field-free region exists between the electrostatic field and the magnetic field.

Filters

These are the simplest form of wavelength selector and are used extensively in colorimeters and simple visible spectrophotometers. Specially selected filters are employed in fluorimeters in order to give a narrow irradiation band and to isolate the fluorescent wavelength.

A filter is a semi-transparent material, usually in the form of a thin glass plate, which is capable of absorbing unwanted electromagnetic radiation and transmitting a narrow band of desired wavelengths. In order to cover a range of wavelengths and give selective transmission a series of different filters is required. The selectivity is achieved by adding a small amount of special materials, such as rare earths, to the glass formulation. Individual filters usually have an effective bandwidth (q.v.) of up to 50 nm, but peak transmittances are as low as 20%.

see also Bandpass filter; Interference filter;
Wratten filter

Fingerprint region (i.r.)
The 7–11 µm (1428–909 cm^{-1}) portion of the infrared spectrum of a substance usually contains a large number of absorption peaks and shows fairly clear differences between even closely related compounds. Although not every absorption peak can always be assigned to particular vibrations in a molecule, the fact that each spectrum is characteristic for the substance from which it has been obtained enables identification to be made by using the spectra in this region as 'fingerprints' and looking for the identical absorption pattern in a library of spectra.

First-order spin pattern (n.m.r.)
This expression is applied to any two coupling groups of protons for which the difference between the chemical shifts (q.v.), Δv, is at least six times the coupling constant J; i.e. $\Delta v > 6J$. Under these conditions the ratios of peak heights in the absorption multiplets are predictable from the Pascal triangle (q.v.). In other cases in which $\Delta v \not> 6J$ the simple multiplet ratios apply less and less as Δv decreases with a corresponding trend away from a first-order pattern.

see also Multiplets

Fishhook symbol (m.s.)
This symbol was introduced[58] to denote the movement of single electrons in molecular and fragment ions as an aid to explaining rearrangement reactions that occur in the mass spectrometer. The full arrow is used to

show the transfer of two electrons. The use of both the fishhook and the full arrow are illustrated in the following reaction sequence:

Fixation pair (em.)
In the use of internal standards (q.v.) in quantitative emission spectroscopy it is usual to compare an emission line of the standard with one from the unknown. If the two lines can only be used under fixed (defined) excitation conditions they are known as a fixation pair. As they respond differently to any change in the excitation a fixation pair can be used to detect any variations in exposure. However, because of the difficulties in maintaining completely reproducible conditions for quantitative studies, it is more common to use an homologous pair (q.v.).

Fixed path-length cell
see Liquid cell

Flameless atomic absorption (a.s.)
see Carbon filament atom reservoir; Massmann furnace

Flame photometer (a.s.)
This instrument is used to study the characteristic radiation obtained from elements when they are introduced into a flame. The intensity of the emission for any particular element is proportional to the concentration.

The flame photometer consists of (a) the nebulizer, (b) the burner, (c) the optical system, (d) the detector and (e) the recorder. In simple flame photometers the monochromation for separate elements is achieved in each case by using a specially selected filter[59]; in more sophisticated instruments a grating is used for monochromation.

The success of flame photometry is greatly dependent upon the flame temperature and the correct filter. It is not usually considered as sensitive a method of analysis as is atomic absorption spectroscopy (q.v.), but this contention has been questioned[60] and in some respects its sensitivity is superior.

Flame source (a.s.)
Both atomic absorption spectroscopy and flame photometry use flames as a common means of exciting samples for spectroscopic studies[61]. Flame temperatures between 2000 and 3000 °C are required for most elements and are attained by burning mixtures of gases such as air and methane or air and acetylene. The sample may be sprayed into the flame or heated in a small crucible (*see* Delves cup).

Attempts have been made to develop a general-purpose gas mixture to obviate the necessity of changing burners and gases to determine different elements. Propane–butane–nitrous oxide and acetylene–nitrous oxide–air are widely applicable and come near to being the ideal mixtures[62].

see also Fuel gases

Fluorescence (pl.)
Fluorescence takes place when an electron in an excited state (q.v.) has failed to lose its excess energy by collisions with other molecules and so returns to a vibrational level in the ground state by the direct release of excess energy. This occurs after a singlet state (q.v.) lifetime of about 10^{-9} s and takes place from the lowest vibrational level of the first excited singlet state. The wavelength of fluorescence spectral bands is theoretically independent of the excitation wavelength although the absolute intensity of fluorescence is dependent on this. Nevertheless, for a substance to exhibit fluorescence the exciting radiation must be of a wavelength that the substance will absorb[63].

The fluorescence spectrum appears on the long-wavelength side of the original absorption band and is nearly always associated with the electron system of an unsaturated molecule. The presence of certain chemicals can lead to quenching (q.v.) of the fluorescence.

see also Triplet state

Fluorescence quantum counter (pl.)
As the fluorescent response of many substances in solution is independent of the wavelength of the incident radiation it is possible to use such fluorophors to measure the quantum intensity of the radiation over a wide spectrum range. The fluorescence quantum counter consists of a solution of the fluorescing material in a detector cell with a path length great enough to absorb all the incident light after it has penetrated only a short path of the total cell path. Any fluorescence produced then has to pass through the

remainder of the solution path length. By this means the solution serves as a filter and only allows the fluorescent wavelength to reach the photocell. The amount of fluorescence is thus a measure of the quantity of incident radiation[64].

Fluorolube (i.r.)

A mixture of fluorinated hydrocarbons used as a mulling agent for solids in infrared spectroscopy. It is specially used to obtain the spectrum in those regions in which Nujol (q.v.) absorption bands appear. By running spectra of mulls (q.v.) prepared with the two individual mulling agents it is possible to obtain the complete spectrum of the sample.

Fluorometer (pl.)

It has been suggested[65] that this name should be used for instruments designed for measuring the lifetime of fluorescent species. In Great Britain the word fluorimeter is more often employed.

see also Spectrofluorimeter

Fluorophor (pl.)

This name is given to any molecule in an excited state that is capable of exhibiting fluorescence (q.v.).

Force constant f (i.r.)

The force constant is defined as the restoring force for a unit displacement from an equilibrium position for a system of two point masses (m_1 and m_2), and is employed in the following expression to obtain values for infrared absorption maxima.

$$\bar{\nu} = \frac{1}{2\pi c} \left(\frac{f}{\dfrac{m_1 m_2}{m_1 + m_2}} \right)^{1/2} \text{cm}^{-1}$$

An approximate value for f is obtained from the expression[66]

$$f = aN \left\{ \frac{\chi_1 \chi_2}{d^2} \right\}^{3/4} + b$$

in which N is the bond order (number of bonds between the two atoms), χ_1 and χ_2 are electronegativities of the atoms, d is the internuclear distance, and a and b constants with values 1·67 and 0·30 respectively.

For a single bond $f \approx 5 \times 10^{-5}$ dyn cm$^{-1} = 5 \times 10^{-9}$ N m^{-1}

For a double bond $f \approx 10 \times 10^{-5}$ dyn cm^{-1} = 10×10^{-9} N m^{-1}

For a triple bond $f \approx 15 \times 10^{-5}$ dyn cm^{-1} = 15×10^{-9} N m^{-1}

Fourier-transform infrared
    see Fourier-transform spectroscopy

Fourier-transform n.m.r.
A method of increasing the sensitivity of n.m.r. spectroscopy first proposed by Ernst and Anderson[67].
    see Fourier-transform spectroscopy

Fourier-transform spectroscopy
The application of Fourier analysis to spectroscopy has led to the development of special instruments designed to give improved spectra. Such instruments study the whole of the selected spectral range all the time in order to give an improved signal to noise ratio compared to traditional instruments employing progressive scanning.

  In far-infrared spectroscopy the Fourier system employs two light beams to produce an interferogram[68,69] which is presented as a digital signal and recorded on punch tape. The final spectrum is obtained from a computer read-out. Some modern instruments possess built-in computers to process the data back directly into a convenient form.

  The technique has also been applied to n.m.r. spectroscopy[67] by subjecting the sample to a series of r.f. pulses and Fourier transforming the free induction decay signals obtained. This increases the sensitivity by a factor of ten and reduces the sweep time necessary.

Fragment ions (m.s.)
Cleavage of bonds in molecular ions in the mass spectrometer (q.v.) leads to the formation of ions from portions of the original molecule. Sometimes these fragments undergo rearrangements before being detected and recorded on the spectrum. Fragment ions are shown as mass/charge peaks lower than the parent molecular peak on the spectrum. Their value is in the indication they give to the nature of groups and substituents in the parent molecule.
    see Bar graph

Franck–Condon principle

Electronic transitions tend to take place from vibrational levels of one electronic state to vibrational levels of other electronic states for which the internuclear distances are the same. These transitions occur at the points at which the kinetic energies of the nuclei are at a minimum, i.e. at the limiting positions of the vibrations. Thus during the transitions there is no appreciable change in internuclear distance or momentum[70].

On a potential energy diagram the change is represented by a vertical line from a vibrational level in one electronic state to a vibrational level in the other electronic state. Absorption of energy is shown by an upward arrow and emission by a downward arrow.

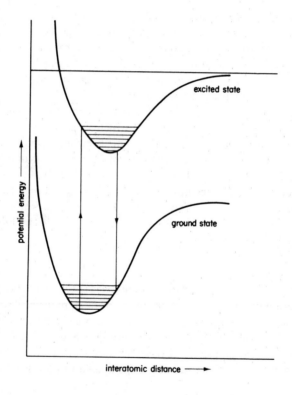

Figure 17. Franck–Condon principle

Freedom, degrees of (i.r.)
        see Degrees of freedom

Free radicals (e.s.r.)
Free radicals come within the classification of systems possessing a net electron spin angular momentum that will give an electron spin resonance spectrum (q.v.). Free radicals are molecules possessing an odd electron, frequently produced by homolytic fission of a chemical bond

$$A:X \longrightarrow A^{\cdot} + X.$$

    molecule   free radicals

    Most free radicals occur as intermediates in chemical reactions and have relatively short lifetimes; stabilization of free radicals and an increase in lifetime can occur in radicals possessing a large degree of unsaturation (e.g. the triphenylmethyl radical) as a result of the distribution of the electron cloud.

Frequency ν
Frequency refers to the number of cycles per unit time and varies inversely with the wavelength:

$$\nu = \frac{c}{\lambda}$$

The SI unit (q.v.) for frequency is the hertz, i.e. cycles per second = hertz (q.v.).

Fuel gases (a.s.)
A wide range of fuel gases have been employed[61,71] in atomic absorption spectroscopy and flame photometry, usually to produce flame temperatures exceeding 2000 °C. In most cases these temperatures can only be obtained by burning the fuel gas with air, oxygen or nitrous oxide as shown in table 3.

Table 3

| | Temperature/°C | | |
Fuel gas	with air	with oxygen	with nitrous oxide
town gas (mainly methane)	1800	2700	
propane	1950	2800	2850
butane	1900	2900	
hydrogen	2050	2650	2650
acetylene	2150	3100	2950
cyanogen	2330	4500	

see also Flames

G

Gallium cut-offs (m.s.)

One method of introducing a liquid sample with a low vapour pressure (< 0.1 torr) into a mass spectrometer is by passing a pipette containing the liquid through a molten metal seal covering a sintered glass disc leading to the reservoir of the sampling unit. The low pressure in the reservoir causes the liquid to flow through the sintered disc. Molten gallium has become the standard material employed for this purpose as it is liquid over the range 30–1983 °C and operating temperatures, commonly up to 400 °C, are beyond the limits of other inlet system seals[72]. Mercury is unsuitable for this purpose because of its high vapour pressure.

Gas cells (i.r.)

To obtain an adequate absorption of infrared radiation by gases and vapours a longer sample path length is required than for liquids and solids. Because of this normal gas cells are about 10 cm long consisting of a glass tube with infrared transparent windows at the ends. For substances possessing low vapour pressures, or available in only small amounts special extended path-length cells are employed. These reflect the infrared radiation back and forth through the vapour by means of a mirror system within the cell and an effective path length of 10 metres or more can be obtained.

Figure 18. Extended path-length gas cell

Gaussian curve (distribution)

The most common frequency distribution for continuous variables is the Gaussian (or normal) distribution; the equation describing this gives the probability at a value x for a set of variables possessing a mean μ and a standard deviation σ.

$$P\{x\} = \frac{1}{(2\pi)^{1/2}\sigma} \exp\left\{-\frac{(x - \mu)_2{}^2}{2\sigma}\right\}$$

The Gaussian curve shape is such that the half-width $W/2$ at half-height $H/2$ are related by the equation

$$\frac{W}{2} = \frac{1\cdot476}{H}$$

Infrared absorption curves correspond to Gaussian shapes, which are symmetrical if recorded on a linear wavenumber abscissa and asymmetric if recorded with a linear wavelength scale.

see also Lorentzian distribution

G.C./M.S. interfaces (m.s.)

see Enrichers; Interfaces

Geissler tubes (pl., u.v.)

Special gas discharge tubes constructed to concentrate the discharge in a capillary tube joining two glass bulbs containing the anode and cathode respectively. The tubes are operated by induction coils and produce intense glow discharges when small quantities of gases or vapours are contained inside the tube.

Getter-ion pump

see Sputter-ion pump

g factor (e.s.r., n.m.r.)

see Landé factor; Nuclear *g* factor

Globar (i.r.)

A distribution of infrared radiation similar to that obtained from a black body (q.v.) is produced from the globar[73]. It is made from sintered silicon carbide shaped into a rod or cylinder about 3 cm long and 6 mm in diameter and is one of the four sources of radiation employed in infrared spectophotometers. The rod is electrically heated between 750 and 1500 °C operating at low voltage and high current; no external preheating is required before it can be used.

cf. Nernst glower; Nichrome source; Opperman source

Golay coils (n.m.r.)

see Shim coils

Golay detector (i.r.)

see Pneumatic cell

Graphite rod (a.s.)
> *see* Carbon filament atom reservoir

Gratings
The conventional diffraction grating consists of a series of closely spaced parallel lines scored onto the surface of a thin glass plate. Spectra are produced by diffraction (q.v.) of the wavefront at the grating surface and the angle (δ) at which these are observed is given by the equation

$$n\lambda = a(\sin \delta \pm \sin i)$$

where a is the distance between adjacent grating lines and i is the angle of incident radiation.

In practice confusion between the first and higher orders of spectra is prevented by removing the higher orders by the use of a filter or prism in the light path. Most modern diffraction gratings for spectroscopy are echelette gratings, a series of fine ridges ruled on a plane surface. Dispersion from gratings is more uniform than that from prisms, and consequently grating spectrophotometers can maintain high resolution over a longer-wavelength period.

For u.v./visible spectrophotometers the gratings used have between 10 000 and 30 000 lines cm^{-1}, whilst in the infrared the range is 100 to 3 000 lines cm^{-1}. Full coverage of the middle-infrared region is frequently obtained by using two gratings, the first to cover the range 4000–1200 cm^{-1} (2·5–8·33 µm) and the other for the 1333–400 cm^{-1} (7·5–2·5 µm) range. Some recent instruments now cover this portion of the infrared with a single grating.

Ground state
When electrons in an atom or molecule occupy the vibrational levels in the lowest possible energy levels, the condition is referred to as the ground state. Absorption of energy leading to an electron being promoted to a higher energy level creates an excited state. At normal temperatures a proportion of atoms is always in excited states as given by the Boltzmann ratio (q.v.).
> cf. Excited state

Gyromagnetic ratio (n.m.r.)
> *see* Magnetogyric ratio

H

Half-wave plates (r.s.)

These are special types of retardation plates (q.v.) used to create half a wavelength (q.v.) or 180° phase difference between the phases of the ordinary and extraordinary components of the polarized light.

Harmonic vibrations (i.r.)

see Overtones

h **bar**

see Planck constant

Heated graphite atomizer (a.s.)

see Carbon filament atom reservoir; Massmann furnace

Heated inlet systems (m.s.)

Solids and liquids possessing low vapour pressures can be introduced into the mass spectrometer by several different heated inlet systems. In some cases the batch inlet system (q.v.) can be used if it is fully heated along its length to the ionization chamber. A direct insertion probe (q.v.) operating at elevated temperatures is frequently used for solids, whilst liquids can be introduced through a molten gallium cut-off (q.v.).

Helmholtz pair (n.m.r.)

see Sweep coils

Hertz Hz (n.m.r.)

This SI unit (q.v.) for frequency has now superseded the former expression cycles per second (c/s). It is used for the number of repetitions of a regular occurrence in one second and is expressed in reciprocal seconds (s^{-1}).

Heterolytic cleavage (m.s.)

Fragmentation of positive ions by transfer of a pair of electrons to one of the fragments is termed heterolytic cleavage. It is represented in mechanistic equations by a full arrow.

$$RCH_2Cl \xrightarrow{-e} RCH_2 \overset{++}{-} \overset{..}{\underset{..}{Cl}} : \longrightarrow RCH_2^+ + : \overset{.}{\underset{..}{Cl}} :$$

cf. Fishhook; Homolytic cleavage

Heteronuclear double resonance (n.m.r.)

Spin–spin decoupling (q.v.) techniques can be applied to identical nuclei (homonuclear) or to different ones (heteronuclear), so that the multiple resonance (q.v.) methods can be used to study the multiplicities arising from the coupling between such dissimilar elements as hydrogen and phosphorus.

Heteronuclear double resonance can obviously be carried out in two ways, either of the two elements being irradiated. The representation $^1H-\{^{31}P\}$ indicates that in studying the proton magnetic spectrum of a substance it is the ^{31}P nucleus that has been decoupled.

cf. Homonuclear double resonance

Higher-order spin patterns (n.m.r.)

see Second-order spin patterns

High-intensity lamps (a.s.)

It has been shown that radiation emitted by hollow cathode lamps (q.v.) results from a two-stage process involving sputtering followed by excitation. In the high-intensity lamps two extra electrodes are built in to produce an additional current across the hollow cathode[74,75]. This assists preferential excitation of the sputtered atoms and has enabled increased sensitivity to be obtained in the determination of some elements.

Hohlraum (i.r.)

This is a laboratory device to produce black-body radiation (q.v.), usually as a standard for comparison with infrared radiation sources. It consists of a closed metal tube, blackened on the inside, with a narrow slit cut into one of the flat ends. On heating the tube the radiation escaping from the slit is virtually identical with that expected from a theoretically black body.

see also Globar; Nernst glower; Nichrome source; Opperman source

Hollow cathode lamp (a.s.)

Despite the fact that electrodeless discharge tubes (q.v.) for some elements are now available the hollow cathode lamp has been the main type of source used for atomic absorption studies up to now[76,77,78]. The lamp is chosen such that the emitting cathode is of the same element as that being studied in the flame. The cathode is in the shape of a cylinder around the anode and is enclosed in a borosilicate or quartz housing containing an inert filler gas, neon or argon, at about 2 mm pressure. The application of a high potential of about 800 V causes a discharge which creates ions of the inert gas. These are accelerated to the cathode and on collision excite the cathode element to emission[6]. Multi-element lamps are also available in which the cathodes are made from alloys or sintered powders.

Figure 19. Hollow cathode lamp

Homogeneity (n.m.r.)

When applied to magnets this refers to the uniformity of the magnetic field around the sample. For high-resolution n.m.r. the magnetic field in this region should not vary by more than 1 part in 10^8. For low-resolution broad-band n.m.r. (q.v.), the acceptable variation is 1 part in 10^5.

Homologous pair (em.)

In the use of emission spectroscopy for quantitative analysis by the internal standard method (q.v.) it is usual to overcome variations in time of exposure and excitation conditions by comparing a line of the unknown with a line of the internal standard possessing roughly the same intensity. These two lines must be such that they are affected in the same way by any changes in the excitation conditions. This means that the ratio of the intensities of these two lines should be constant even if there are variations in exposure or development.

cf. Fixation pair

Homolytic cleavage (m.s.)

Fragmentation of ions in mass spectrometry frequently involves single electron transfers to each of the two resulting fragments. This is termed homolytic cleavage and the single electron movements are indicated by fishhooks (q.v.) as shown in the equation below:

homolytic cleavage

cf. Heterolytic cleavage

Homonuclear double resonance (n.m.r.)

Spin–spin decoupling applied to identical nuclei can be carried out using multiple resonance techniques (q.v.). Under these conditions when the nuclei are isotopically identical it is called homonuclear double resonance. It is represented by $^1H—\{^1H\}$ indicating that the proton within the brackets is the one that has been irradiated and therefore decoupled.

cf. Heteronuclear double resonance

65

Hooke law (i.r., r.s.)

In its normal form this law states that an elastic body suffers a strain that is proportional to the stress imposed upon it. In more general terms this can be expressed to mean that the elongation of an elastic object will be proportional to the force applied to it.

The law is equally applicable to the vibrational nature of molecular bonds and under these conditions it is possible to employ an equation relating the frequency of the oscillation, the force constant of the bond (q.v.) and the masses of the two atoms:

$$v = \frac{1}{2\pi} \left(\frac{f}{\dfrac{m_1 m_2}{m_1 + m_2}} \right)^{1/2}$$

Hybrid T (e.s.r.)

This arrangement of tubular waveguides (q.v.) is used in e.s.r. spectrometers to prevent the microwave power from the klystron oscillator (q.v.) from passing straight to the crystal detector.

Energy directed from the klystron to arm A is split equally in two directions through the arms B and C to the balancing load and resonant cavity respectively. No power reaches arm D, the crystal detector, if B and C are balanced. But when an e.s.r. absorption occurs in the cavity the system is out of balance and this results in a signal from C which passes to the detector in D.

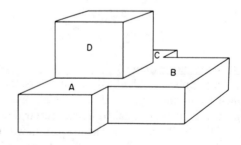

Figure 20. Hybrid T

Hydrogen bonds

Hydrogen atoms attached to atoms possessing unpaired electrons, such as oxygen and nitrogen, are able to undergo a weak form of association with groups possessing easily polarized electrons. The hydrogen atom, whilst being held by its former atom is attracted to the second group and in molecular structures this is represented by a dotted line between the two atoms, e.g. $-OH \ldots \ldots :O=C<$.

These associations may occur between atoms in the same molecule, intramolecular hydrogen bonding, or between atoms in different molecules, intermolecular hydrogen bonding. The existence of hydrogen bonding gives rise to characteristic absorptions in spectra; it is particularly noticed in infrared spectra[79] for example as the broad band between 3700 cm^{-1} and 3200 cm^{-1} (between 2·7 μm and 3·1 μm) which is usually assigned to H-bonded OH stretching vibrations.

Hydrogen discharge lamp (u.v.)

Radiation for the ultraviolet region of the spectrum is provided by means of a discharge lamp filled with hydrogen. The upper range of the lamp is about 440 nm and the lower range is 200 nm if the lamp has quartz walls; it can be extended to 185 nm if fused silica walls are fitted. The intensity of the lamp can be almost trebled if deuterium is used in place of hydrogen.

cf. Tungsten filament lamp

Hyperchromic effect (u.v.)

If structural modification leads to an increase in the molar extinction coefficient (q.v.) for a particular chromophoric group it is said to have brought about an hyperchromic effect. The hyperchromic effect frequently accompanies a bathochromic shift (q.v.).

cf. Hypochromic effect

Hyperfine splitting (e.s.r.)

In e.s.r. spectra the hyperfine splitting observed arises owing to interactions between the electron spin and the spins of the adjacent magnetic nuclei. A nucleus possessing a spin quantum number I will split each electronic energy level into $2I + 1$ levels and produce that number of lines in the

spectrum. For *n* equivalent nuclei $2nI + 1$ resonance lines are produced. Both ^1H and ^{14}N nuclei lead to hyperfine splitting, but ^{12}C and ^{16}O do not.
see also Electron spin resonance; Fermi contact interaction

Hypochromic effect (u.v.)

Structural modification leading to a decrease in the molar extinction coefficient (q.v.) for a particular chromophoric group is called a hypochromic effect. The hypochromic effect frequently accompanies a hypsochromic shift (q.v.).
cf. Hyperchromic effect

Hypsochromic shift (u.v.)

Structural modification in a molecule which leads to a characteristic maximal absorption being displaced towards shorter wavelength (higher frequency) is said to have brought about a hypsochromic shift. This is often referred to as a blue shift.
cf. Bathochromic shift

I

I (n.m.r.)

see Spin quantum number

Incandescence (i.r., pl.)

Materials are said to exhibit incandescence if they are self-luminous solely owing to their high temperatures. Such substances produce continuous emission spectra covering a very wide range of wavelengths from the ultraviolet to the infrared. In some cases the distribution of energy in the spectrum approaches that of a black body (q.v.); in these instances such materials are useful as sources for infrared spectrophotometers.

INDOR (n.m.r.)

Internuclear double resonance (INDOR) is a variation on the simple multiple resonance (q.v.) technique specially applicable to weak signals such as ^{13}C satellites. For this purpose the radio-frequency field is adjusted to satisfy the resonance conditions for one nucleus whilst a second radio frequency is used to sweep the spectrum for a second nucleus as the absorption for the first nucleus is observed. If the two nuclei are normally coupled then under these conditions the observed INDOR spectrum, for the first nucleus, consists of a series of negative peaks. This will occur when the second radio-frequency field corresponds to the energy levels of the system being observed[80,81].

Induction method (n.m.r.)

This method of detecting n.m.r. absorption signals, sometimes called the double-coil method, was first used by Bloch[82]. It employs two coils arranged at right angles to each other such that the detector coil picks up signals arising from the re-emission of energy imparted to the nuclei by the irradiation coil.

Figure 21. Cross-coil probe

Infrared detectors

A wide range of infrared detectors exists to cover the wavelengths from near- to far-infrared regions. Recent developments in this field have included detectors operating at low temperatures (superconducting bolometers), and rapid response detectors producing signals faster than 1 ns[83].

> *see also* Bolometer; Photoelectric detectors; Pneumatic cell; Thermocouple

Infrared radiation sources
see Globar; Nernst glower; Nichrome source; Opperman source; Tungsten lamp

Infrared spectra
With recent improvements in instrumentation the infrared region of the electromagnetic spectrum (q.v.) is now considered to cover the range from approximately 12 500 to 10 cm^{-1} (0·80–1000 μm).

It is generally subdivided into three sections: near-infrared, arising from electronic, plus vibrational and rotational transitions, 12 500–4000 cm^{-1} (0·80–2·5 μm), this is also the overtone and combination band (q.v.) region; middle (fundamental) infrared, from vibrational plus rotational transitions, 4000–200 cm^{-1} (2·5–50 μm); far-infrared, rotational transitions, 200–10 cm^{-1} (50–1000 μm).

The middle-infrared region is the one most commonly employed for standard laboratory investigations, the portion between 1428 and 909 cm^{-1} (7·0 and 11·0 μm) being known as the 'fingerprint region' (q.v.).

Studies beyond 200 cm^{-1} require special instruments and techniques[84], such as the use of caesium iodide prisms and Fourier-transform procedures (q.v.).

Figure 22. Infrared spectrum of indene

Integration n.m.r.)
Integration is the process by which the relative areas under spectral peaks are measured and compared. In the case of n.m.r. spectra the integration consists of a series of steps usually run as an overlapping trace to the original spectrum. The heights of the integration steps correspond to the number of nuclei in the groups producing the absorption peaks.

Interfaces (m.s.)
A number of approaches have been made to obtain mass spectra from chromatographic effluents, and these have necessitated the development of interfacial systems to remove the carrier gas and leave an enriched sample[85]. Some of the systems use porous tubes designed to allow progressive loss of the carrier gas; another approach has been the use of a silicone rubber diaphragm which permits preferential penetration by organic materials.
see also Watson–Biemann separator

Interference
If two or more wave motions meet in such a way that the individual waves reinforce or oppose each other the resulting wave pattern is referred to as an interference pattern. If two waves of equal wavelength and amplitude are out of phase by half a wavelength along a common path of motion, they will cancel each other out.

Because electromagnetic radiation is not continuous, but released in quanta, the waves producing interference must be produced from a common source. For this reason a beam splitter is used in interferometers in which this phenomenon is employed.

Fourier-transform (q.v.) infrared spectrometry uses an interference procedure to obtain an interferogram from the spectrum studied.

Interference filters
An interference filter is made by sandwiching a thin layer of a transparent dielectric possessing a low refractive index, such as magnesium fluoride, between very thin silver films which are partially transparent. Any incident light that passes through the silver layers undergoes internal reflection between the two silver films, complete interference taking place when the path difference is some multiple of half a wavelength. The transmitted

region is a narrow band with its maximum at this wavelength as any other wavelength is reflected away. The maximum transmittance from an interference filter is about 50% with a bandwidth of between 10 nm and 17 nm.

Multi-layer interference filters consist of alternate layers of high and low refractive index materials.

Internal conversion (pl.)

This is the term given to the process by which a molecule goes from a low vibrational level of a high energy state to a high vibrational level of a lower energy state with nearly the same total energy. It is from this lower state that a return to the ground state can occur by the emission of fluorescence (q.v.).

Internal reference (n.m.r.)

When the n.m.r. reference material (e.g. TMS for proton spectra) is dissolved in the same solvent as the sample under investigation it is being employed as an internal reference. Under these conditions it experiences the identical effects of the magnetic field as does the sample. Results are slightly more accurate by using the reference in this way than they are when it is used as an external reference (q.v.).

Internal reflectance spectroscopy (i.r.)

see Attenuated total reflectance

Internal standard

Quantitative analysis employing internal standards is used in several realms of spectroscopy including infrared, emission and atomic absorption. It involves adding a fixed amount of an internal standard both to a series of increasing concentrations of reference sample and to the unknown concentration. A calibration line is plotted of the ratio of the absorption of the characteristic line of the reference samples and the absorption of the characteristic line of the internal standard against the known concentrations of the reference samples.

This ideally gives a straight-line plot and the unknown sample concentration can be established by determining the position of the corresponding ratio of the sample absorption and internal standard on the calibration line.

In quantitative infrared analysis on solids the internal standard most commonly employed is potassium thiocyanate. It is used as a 1–2% mixture in potassium bromide for making pressed discs (q.v.). The thiocyanate shows a characteristic absorption at 2125 cm^{-1} (4·7 μm) which rarely interferes with absorptions of samples under investigation[86]. The internal standard method has also been applied to mulls[87] (q.v.).

Intersystem crossing (pl.)
The populating of the triplet state (q.v.) can take place by a molecule 'crossing' from a low vibrational energy level of a singlet state (q.v.) to an upper vibrational level of a triplet state. Such a process is referred to as an intersystem crossing and takes about 10^{-7} to 10^{-8} s. It eventually leads to phosphorescence (q.v.) as electrons can remain for extended periods of time in the triplet state.

Ion
Individual atoms and combined groups of atoms and molecules which have acquired a net positive or negative charge through losing or gaining one or more electrons are called ions. They are of special interest in mass spectrometry (q.v.) and in electron spin resonance spectroscopy (q.v.).

Ion abundancies (m.s.)
Fragmentation of molecules in mass spectrometers gives rise to other positive ions which are recorded as the mass spectra of the molecules. The size of the peak recorded at a particular mass/charge value is related to the number of those particular ions detected at that value. So that the relative heights of the various peaks in any mass spectrum is a measure of the relative ion abundancies. The largest peak in the spectrum is called the base peak (q.v.) and all other peaks are expressed as a percentage of the base peak. The relative abundancies of the major peaks in a mass spectrum are represented diagrammatically on a bar graph (q.v.).

Ionization efficiency curve (m.s.)
This is a plot of the relationship between the production of molecular ions (the ionization efficiency) against the electron energy (eV) of the ionization

source. Its importance to mass spectrometry is that the ionization efficiency starts to rise at the ionization energy (q.v.) of the molecule and reaches a plateau between about 50 to 70 eV. For this reason most mass spectrometers are operated at about 70 eV for general usage as any voltage fluctuation does not affect the reproducibility of the spectra.

Ionization energy (a.s.)
In general the ionization energy is the energy necessary to remove an electron from an atom. It is normal to refer particularly to the first ionization energy as that required to remove the most loosely bound electron from the atom to form an ion. In flame photometry ionization of atoms leads to a decrease in the number of neutral metal atoms in the flame and hence results in a corresponding weakness of the atomic spectral lines. At about 2700 °C some elements are almost one hundred per cent ionized.

Ionization energy (m.s.)
The energy required to remove an electron from a molecule varies from one substance to another. For organic compounds the ionization energy is generally between 8 and 15 eV, being the energy needed to create an ion from the molecule existing in the ground vibrational level of the lowest electronic state. This is often referred to as the 'adiabatic ionization energy' as the change from the molecular state to the molecular ion does not usually occur between the lowest vibrational levels; the measured ionization energy will, therefore, differ slightly from this theoretical value[88].

Ion sources (m.s.)
>*see* Electron bombardment ion source; Isatron;
>Knudsen cell furnace; Laser microprobe; Photo-
>ionization source; Spark ionization source;
>Thermal emission ion source

Iris diaphragm
This is frequently used in fluorimeters to control the amount of radiation from the source; the iris diaphragm consists of a series of overlapping plates arranged to move so that a roughly circular opening of variable size is

produced. This is achieved by maintaining a nearly constant angle between the edges of adjacent plates.

Irtran (i.r.)
This is the trade name for a series of infrared cell windows made by Eastman Kodak. They are carefully selected fluorides, selenides and sulphides impervious to acids and alkalis for use with aqueous solutions within the spectral range $5000-333$ cm^{-1} ($0.2-30$ μm). They can also be used at elevated temperatures up to 300 °C.

The most general type is made from zinc sulphide with a long-wave transmission limit of 60% for a 1 cm thickness at 645.2 cm^{-1} (15.5 μm).

Isatron (m.s.)
The isatron is a high-precision electron bombardment ion source (q.v.) used in mass spectrometry[51]. It measures 3 cm long and 2 cm in diameter and is constructed to focus a concentrated electron beam onto the gaseous molecules.

Isobaric fragments (m.s.)
On low-resolution mass spectrometers any single peak is likely to represent several different ions formed from the fragmentation process. Ions possessing a common mass/charge ratio, and therefore producing a single peak, are termed isobaric; e.g. N_2^+, CO^+, and $C_2H_4^+$ are isobaric at (m/e) 28.

Isobestic point
On a series of overlapping spectral curves for a binary mixture obtained with the two components in differing proportions there is one point, and sometimes more, at which all the curves are coincidental. At this isobestic point the absorption is, therefore, a constant for all concentration ratios for the two substances in the binary mixture.

An isobestic point is of particular value as a reference point in quantitative i.r. or u.v. studies and can usually be observed in reaction rate studies in which one species is diminishing and another increasing in concentration. This may be seen in the illustration below.

75

Isotopic abundance (m.s.)

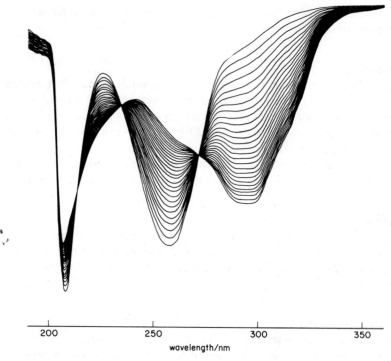

wavelength/nm

Figure 23. Isobestic points obtained for the rearrangement of a
norbornene derivative

Isotopic abundance (m.s.)

The presence of heavy isotopes leads to the occurrence of mass spectral
peaks of higher value than that corresponding to the molecular ion peak
(*see* Parent peak). Such peaks are designated $P + 1$, $P + 2$, etc., and
their magnitudes relative to the parent peak are related to the proportion
of the higher isotopes present and differ according to the molecular formula
of the compound. Isotopic abundance tables[4] giving calculated $P + 1$ and
$P + 2$ values for a wide range of chemical formulae are used as a guide
to the true chemical formula of unknown compounds by comparison with
the sizes of the peaks measured from the mass spectrum of the substance.

see also Abundance tables; Bar graph

IUPAC

The International Union of Pure and Applied Chemistry has been responsible for coordinating the standardization of signs and nomenclature employed in chemistry in order to improve international communication.

J

J (n.m.r.)

J is the symbol used to denote the spin–spin coupling constant (q.v.) and represents the magnitude of the separation between the peaks of a multiplet arising from the coupling. The value of *J* is always expressed in hetrz (q.v.).

K

Karplus equation (n.m.r.)

The dihedral angle (Φ) between vicinal protons can be calculated approximately from the coupling constant of the two protons by the use of this equation originally proposed by Karplus[89,90].

$$J = 8{\cdot}5 \cos^2 \Phi - 0{\cdot}28 \qquad \text{if } 0° \leqslant \Phi \leqslant 90°$$

$$J = 9{\cdot}5 \cos^2 \Phi - 0{\cdot}28 \qquad \text{if } 90° < \Phi \leqslant 180°$$

The calculation has to be modified to allow for the effects of other substituents close to the vicinal protons and several variations on the equations have been developed.

Kayser K (i.r.)

This term is no longer recommended for spectroscopic measurements. It was originally suggested for the unit of wavenumber (q.v.) by the Joint

77

K bands (u.v.)

Commission for Spectroscopy but considerable controversy arose[91,92], and it has not been adopted as an SI unit (q.v.).

$$1 \text{ K} = 1 \text{ cm}^{-1}$$

K bands (u.v.)

One of the systems of designation[13] of bands in ultraviolet/visible spectroscopy uses this symbol to refer to absorptions arising from $\pi \rightarrow \pi^*$ transitions usually having high molar extinction coefficients, $\varepsilon > 10\,000$. These occur in conjugated systems, particularly aromatic compounds. (K is from the German meaning kongugierte.)

see also Bands (ultraviolet)

KBr pellet (i.r.)

One method of studying solid samples in infrared spectroscopy is by preparing a pressed disc (q.v.), by compressing a finely ground mixture of the sample and potassium bromide. As the potassium bromide does not absorb in the middle-infrared region the only absorption obtained is that due to the sample.

cf. Mulls

Klystron oscillator (e.s.r.)

Signal generators employed in electron spin resonance spectrometers are usually of the klystron type operating in the Q (8 mm) or X (3 cm) microwave bands. The klystron is a vacuum tube which produces an electron beam from a heated cathode. A high positive potential attracts this beam into the microwave cavity in which electric field variations create oscillations which lead to bunching of the electrons in place of the formerly homogeneous beam. From the resonance cavity the electron bunches pass to a repeller electrode, negative with respect to the cathode, which returns them to the cavity.

Oscillation of the system is maintained by employing suitable voltages and energy is then fed from the klystron to a waveguide (q.v.) which conducts it to the hybrid T (q.v.) from which it passes to the sample under investigation in the magnetic field.

The klystron is also used in conjunction with the electrodeless discharge tube source in atomic absorption spectroscopy.

Knudsen cell furnace (m.s.)
This device is used to produce a fine molecular beam for study by mass spectrometry. It consists of a small tungsten or tantalum crucible contained in a high-temperature furnace surrounded by a water-cooled housing. The sample is heated to 2500 °C by electrical heating under high vacuum and the resulting stream of molecules is directed through a minute effusion hole (< 1 mm in diameter) across the line of direction of the electron beam in the ionization chamber[51].

It is used particularly for thermodynamic studies on solids at elevated temperatures, and has been employed for vapour pressure investigations on silver and graphite[93].

KRS-5 (i.r.)
Specially developed for use as a prism medium for infrared spectrometers KRS-5 is a mixture of thallium bromide and thallium iodide with molar percentages of 45·7 and 54·3 respectively[94].
see also Prisms, infrared

L

Lambert law (i.r., u.v.)
For homogeneous substances the portion of incident radiant energy absorbed is proportional to the thickness of the absorbing material[21,22].
Mathematically this is expressed as

$$- \frac{dI}{dl} \propto I$$

which on integration becomes

$$\log \frac{I_0}{I} = k_1 l$$

see also Beer–Lambert law; Absorbance

Landé factor g (e.s.r.)

The Landé, or *g*, factor is sometimes called the spectroscopic splitting factor. It is a dimensionless constant which is a physical property of the electron, being a proportionality constant between the magnetic moment and the angular momentum.

$g \approx 2$ for particles with pure electronic spin.

$g \approx 1$ for particles with pure electronic orbital magnetism.

More exactly $g = 2 \cdot 002\ 319$ for unbound electrons and variations of the *g* factor from this value are often considered as being analogous to chemical shifts in n.m.r. as they depend upon the chemical environment of the unpaired electron.

cf. Nuclear *g* factor

Larmor frequency ω_L (n.m.r.)

Another name for the angular frequency of electron precession (q.v.). It is related to the magnetogyric ratio (q.v.) and the applied field by the following equation:

$$\omega_L = \frac{eB}{2m_e}$$

It is now usual to differentiate between the Larmor frequency—applicable to electrons—and the nuclear angular precession frequency (q.v.) for nuclei.

Laser (r.s.)

The word LASER is constructed from the expression Light Amplification by Stimulated Emission of Radiation which roughly describes the nature of the device[95]. The laser may take many forms, but the simplest is the ruby laser consisting to all intents and purposes of an aluminium oxide matrix containing some Cr^{3+} ions. The crystal is highly polished at each end and acts as an optical resonator.

Energy from a flash lamp passes into the crystal; this leads to a rapid build-up of energy and the creation of metastable states eventually producing a population inversion (q.v.). The reversion of one active species automatically stimulates other active species to release energy and a rapid amplification occurs. The powerful beam of radiation escapes as a burst of energy from one end of the rod. The resulting beam is monochromatic, coherent and parallel[96].

Many lasers now use gases rather than crystals. These have the advantage that they can produce a number of different wavelengths; the argon laser for example having eight suitable radiations. Gas lasers are often preferred for their continuous steady power, the helium–neon laser for instance giving less than 1 % variation in output.

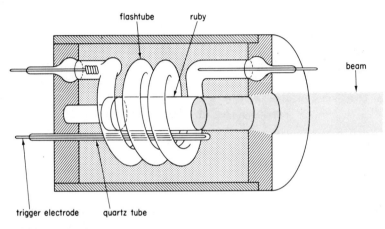

flashtube   ruby

beam

trigger electrode   quartz tube

Figure 24. Ruby laser

Laser beam excitation
This is a general expression employed when lasers are used as a means of heating small samples in order to bring about excitation or ionization.

Laser microprobe (em., m.s.)
Sample excitation for emission spectroscopy applicable to non-conducting materials can be achieved by focusing the beam from a laser (q.v.) onto a small amount of sample. About 20% of the laser beam energy is used in exciting the atoms in the material studied[97]; the vapour from the sample is used to short circuit the gap between the electrodes on the emission spectrometer thus producing the spectrum.

The laser microprobe is also being used in mass spectrometry to vaporize sample directly into the ion source[98,99]. A spot size of up to 800 μm is made on a pellet of the sample held on the end of a probe inserted through a vacuum lock.

81

Laser Raman spectroscopy
Raman spectroscopy has advanced rapidly since the laser was first introduced as the source of excitation[100]. The advantages of the laser are that it produces a powerful beam of monochromatic, coherent radiation vastly superior to that obtained with other Raman sources[95,96] such as the Toronto arc (q.v.).

Lattice (n.m.r.)
An expression referring to the total environment around a nucleus including the adjacent molecular structure and the solvent.

Lead sulphide conductive cell
> *see* Photoelectric infrared detectors

Leak valve (m.s.)
> *see* Molecular leak

Ligand field theory (u.v.)
When a transition metal ion is attached to water molecules, or any other ligand, electronic transitions can occur between the different groups of degenerate d orbitals. This absorption of energy gives rise to the characteristic colours of transition metal compounds that are studied in ultraviolet/visible spectroscopy. This explanation of the colour of these compounds is the basis of the ligand field theory[101].

Light
In its correct sense this refers to the specific part of the electromagnetic spectrum (q.v.) covering the visible region that is normally associated with human vision. It extends from the violet (380 nm) to the red (780 nm) and is commonly studied jointly with the ultraviolet region (q.v.).
> *see also* Velocity of light

Light (monochromatic)
Meaning specifically light of one wavelength this is the ideal state required after monochromation has been carried out in the spectrometer. In most cases this is rarely attained, as irrespective of the quality of the optics in the instrument there is still a finite slit width. As a result most so-called mono-

chromatic light actually covers a narrow band on either side of the required line.

see also Effective bandwidth

Line spectra (a.s., em.)
These are the characteristic spectra of atoms resulting from changes in the energy levels of the electrons. They consist of a large number of irregularly spaced lines.

see also Atomic spectra

Liquid cell (i.r.)
Liquid cells for infrared spectroscopy can be of fixed or variable path length. A substance of molecular weight about 200 in 1 % solution gives satisfactory spectra with 1·0 mm path length; a standard cell of this thickness is filled by 0·4 ml of solution. For experimental reasons cells can be either permanently built or demountable for assembly when required. A variety of spacers is available permitting selection of path lengths between 0·05 mm and 3·0 mm. Cells are normally designed for syringe filling. Variable pathlength cells, for accurate compensation work and for quantitative studies, are designed around a vernier screw thread which enables the path length to be adjusted at will.

cf. Microcells

Figure 25. Fixed path-length cell

Figure 26. Variable path-length cell

Liquid filters (r.s.)

Monochromation of radiation from arc and lamp sources in Raman spectroscopy is carried out using various solutions to absorb unwanted radiation and to isolate the required exciting line. Typical liquid filters that have been used are saturated sodium nitrite or praseodymium chloride in aqueous solution and p-nitrotoluene in ethanol.

Littrow mounting

Double dispersion and resolution are achieved by the combination of a mirror and prism as a monochromator such that any refracted beam is reflected back through the prism. In the case of quartz prisms this obviates the need for both left- and right-handed quartz as in the Cornu mounting (q.v.).

Monochromation in the Littrow mounting is achieved either by rotating the prism and mirror simultaneously, or by just rotating the mirror. In some cases a separate mirror is avoided by silvering one surface of the prism.

The system has been used extensively in a wide range of spectrometers.

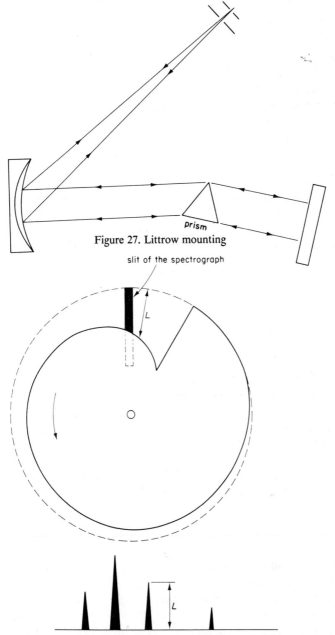

Figure 27. Littrow mounting

slit of the spectrograph

Figure 28. Log sector (appearance of spectrum lines of different intensity indicated below)

Log sector (em.)
Both the log sector and the step sector (q.v.) are used to obtain a gradation of intensity of emission spectral lines in order to establish the exposure/line characteristics for photographic emulsion on emission plates[102]. They can also be used to compare relative intensities of different lines and for quantitative emission spectroscopy, figure 28.

Lone pair electrons
Electron pairs which whilst not involved in bond formation in a particular compound but are capable of taking part in forming a coordinate bond with a substance possessing an incomplete octet are called 'lone pairs'. Ammonia is a typical example of a substance possessing a lone pair and is capable of forming a bond with compounds such as boron trifluoride.

$$
\begin{array}{cc}
\text{H} & \text{F} \\
\text{×·} & \text{×·} \\
\text{H}^{×}_{×}\text{N:} + & \text{B}^{×}_{.}\text{F} \longrightarrow \text{H}_3\text{N:BF}_3 \\
\text{·×} & \text{·×} \\
\text{H} & \text{F}
\end{array}
$$

Longitudinal relaxation T_1 (n.m.r.)
Also known as spin–lattice relaxation, this is one process by which nuclear spin energy is lost and occurs by transfer to the molecular environment. The energy is lost by localized variable magnetic fields to other magnetic nuclei. Impurities in the n.m.r. sample, particularly paramagnetic species, greatly increase the rate of relaxation. Broadening of absorption peaks due to spin–lattice relaxation occurs if T_1 is less than 10^{-3} s. Liquid samples rarely exhibit broadening of the absorption peaks as T_1 in these cases is usually greater than 10^{-2} s.
cf. Transverse relaxation

Long-range coupling (n.m.r.)
Spin–spin coupling (q.v.) for protons usually extends only over three bond lengths. However, coupling beyond this is possible and occurs frequently in unsaturated systems, such as allenes. Over this extended range, of four or five bond lengths, the coupling constants are usually less than 3 Hz.

Lorentzian curve (distribution) (e.s.r., n.m.r.)
The shapes of the absorption and dispersion lines which may be calculated from the Bloch equations (q.v.) are known as Lorentzian curves and are those expected under ideal circumstances. In practice the theoretical shapes are rarely obtained in n.m.r. spectra due to instrumental variations and sample inhomogeneities.

Lorentzian (also known as Cauchy) curves differ from Gaussian curves (q.v.) in that they tail more on either side of the central distribution, the half-width $W/2$ at half-height $H/2$ being given by the equation

$$\frac{W}{2} = \frac{1}{\pi H}$$

The equation governing the Lorentzian distribution of the probability at a value x for a set of variables is

$$P(x) = \frac{1}{\pi} \frac{a}{a^2 + (x - b)^2}$$

where $a > 0$, and $-\infty < x < +\infty$.

Luminescence (pl.)
Luminescence is a collective word used to cover all forms of light emission other than those arising from elevated temperature. Any system exhibiting luminescence is losing energy in the form of emitted radiation. It is subdivided into fluorescence (q.v.) in which the excited state exists for less than 10^{-8} s, and phosphorescence (q.v.) in which the excited state lasts for more than 10^{-8} s. All processes of luminescence involve three steps—absorption, change in energy state and emission, which may be brought about by a wide variety of processes, e.g. photoluminescence (q.v.) by photons and chemiluminescence (q.v.) in chemical reactions.

Lyman series (em.)

see Atomic spectra

M

McLafferty rearrangements (m.s.)

Fragmentation in mass spectrometers frequently involves rearrangement processes within the ions created. The McLafferty rearrangement[103] is a six-centre transfer of hydrogen. This is shown by the following process with methyl propyl ketone (pentan-2-one):

Magic T (e.s.r.)

see Hybrid T

Magnetic deflection mass spectrometer (m.s.)

Mass spectra can be obtained by the exclusive use of a magnetic field for resolution of the accelerated positive ions as in a single-focusing mass spectrometer (q.v.), or by using the magnetic field in conjunction with an electrostatic field in double-focusing mass spectrometers (q.v.). The angles of deflection used for the magnetic fields may be 60°, 90°, 120° or 180°, the ions being separated according to their mass/charge ratios satisfying the equation

$$\frac{m}{e} = \frac{H^2 r^2}{2V}$$

Individual ionic species are brought to a focus by varying either H or V.

Magnetic field strength H

This is the intensity of a magnetic field at a point and is the force that would exist on a unit north magnetic pole at that point. It is related to the magnetic flux density (q.v.) and permeability by the equation

$$H = \frac{B}{\mu}$$

In SI units (q.v.) the magnetic field strength is measured in ampere per metre. 1 A m^{-1} corresponding to 4×10^{-3} oersted.

Magnetic flux Φ

see Weber

Magnetic flux density *B*

This is also known as magnetic induction; it is the magnetic flux per unit area perpendicular to the lines of flux. The SI unit (q.v.) for this quantity is the tesla, defined as kg s^{-2} A^{-1} = Wb m^{-2}.

$$1 \text{ T} = 10^4 \text{ gauss}$$

Magnetic induction

see Magnetic flux density

Magnetic moment μ (n.m.r.)

This is the turning force (torque) operating on a magnet when it is held at right angles to a field of unit intensity and is equal to the product of the magnetic pole strength and the distance between the poles. It is measured in ampere per square metre.

$$1 \text{ A m}^{-2} = 10^3 \text{ e.m.u. s}^{-1}$$

Magnetization *M*

This is the magnetic moment of a magnet per unit volume and is given by the equation

$$M = \frac{B}{\mu_0} - H$$

Magnetogyric ratio γ (n.m.r.)

The magnetogyric ratio is defined as the ratio between the magnetic moment (q.v.) and the angular momentum:

$$\gamma = \frac{\mu 2\pi}{Ih}$$

Under the SI scheme (q.v.) the magnetogyric ratio is measured in kg s^{-3} A^{-1} = s^{-1} T^{-1}. For protons the value of γ is $2 \cdot 675 \times 10^8$ s^{-1} T^{-1}.

89

Magneton

    see Bohr magneton; Nuclear magneton

Marker peaks (i.r.)

    see Calibration peaks

Maser (r.s.)

MASER is an abbreviation for Microwave Amplification by Stimulated Emission of Radiation.

    see Laser

Mass analyser (m.s.)

The portion of a mass spectrometer that produces the resolution of the positive ions is known as the mass analyser. In most instruments this will be simply a magnetic field, although in a double-focusing mass spectrometer it will also include an electrostatic field. The mass analyser in a time-of-flight (q.v.) instrument is a horizontal tube known as the drift tube (q.v.).

Mass/charge ratio (m.s.)

A mass spectrometer (q.v.) actually measures mass/charge ratios rather than absolute mass values and it is these that are recorded on the mass spectrum. As the majority of positive ions produced carry a single charge there is usually no difficulty in interpreting the spectra. However, this is not invariably the case and most spectra of organic compounds include some peaks due to doubly (or even triply) charged ions. In these cases the spectral peak occurs at a half (or one-third) the true mass value. The existence of a doubly charged ion can easily be determined in those cases in which the true mass value is an odd number as the observed mass/charge ratio is found at a half mass value.

    see also Metastable ions

Massmann furnace (a.s.)

This flameless method of atomization used in atomic absorption spectroscopy is a carbon tube atom reservoir and was the forerunner of the present heated graphite atomizers. It consists of a hollow graphite cylinder about 50 mm long and 10 mm in diameter situated so that the radiation beam passes along the axis of the tube[106]. The sample (1–200 μl) is placed in the middle of the tube through a small hole. By passing a small current through the graphite tube the sample is first evaporated, then atomized by applying a much higher current (500 A at 10 V). Oxidation of the graphite is prevented by maintaining it in a nitrogen or argon atmosphere.

see also Carbon filament atom reservoir; Delves cup;
Tantalum boat

Mass spectrograph (m.s.)
An instrument in which positive ions are separated according to their mass/charge ratios and used to produce images on a photographic plate. Such instruments are commonly used to study isotopic abundancies in elements. The early mass studies carried out by Thomson[104] and Aston[105] used photographic plates to detect the ions.

Mass spectrometer (m.s.)
In a mass spectrometer the positive ions are separated according to their mass/charge ratios and the individual ionic species detected and recorded electronically[88]. The various ions are indicated on the spectral chart as peaks of different sizes corresponding to the quantities of the individual ions produced. The spectrometer consists of the following distinct parts: the inlet system, the ion source (q.v.), the accelerating slits (q.v.), the mass analyser (q.v.), the ion collector and the recorder.

Mass spectrum (m.s.)
This may be either in the form of a photographic record, as produced by a mass spectrograph (q.v.), or as a chart record of the type obtained from a mass spectrometer (q.v.). In either case the spectrum is a record of the mass/charge ratios of the positively charged ions plotted against their relative abundancies. As the size and nature of the ions produced is dependent upon the molecular structure the mass spectrum is characteristic for that substance under the defined spectrometric conditions.

see also Bar graph

Mattauch–Herzog mass analyser (m.s.)
This arrangement for a double-focusing mass analyser (q.v.) consists of a 32° 50′ electrostatic field deflecting the ions in one direction followed by a 90° magnetic field turning them back in the opposite direction. The electrostatic field serves to produce a beam of ions possessing uniform energies

91

which are then focused according to their mass/charge ratios by the magnetic field.

see also Nier–Johnson mass analyser

Maxwell–Boltzmann distribution and statistics

Maxwell–Boltzmann statistics is the name given to the distribution equations developed separately by Maxwell and Boltzmann before the introduction of quantum mechanics. Several different forms of the equations exist[107], the most common being that the number of molecules $N(v)$ with velocities between v and $v + dv$ is given by

$$N(v) = 4\pi N \left(\frac{m}{2\pi kT}\right)^{3/2} e^{-mv^2/2kT} v^2 \, dv$$

Meker burner (a.s.)

see Burner

Mercury diffusion pump (m.s.)

Maintenance of high vacua in mass spectrometers is achieved by using a combination of an oil pump (the fore-pump) and a mercury diffusion pump. The mercury pump works on the principle of heated mercury vapour being condensed by a cooling system and in so doing dragging with it the molecules of gas remaining in the system. For this purpose the mercury diffusion pump is situated between the backing pump and the evacuated vessel. The condensed mercury runs towards the backing pump and is eventually led back to the boiler reservoir.

see also Sputter-ion pump

Metastable ions (m.s.)

Mass spectra (q.v.) frequently include diffuse peaks possessing non-integral mass/charge values[108]. These arise from ions which have decomposed after they have been accelerated from the ion source and before they have been resolved by the analyser. As such they have been accelerated as one species (the metastable ion) and resolved as another (the daughter ion).

The process is

$$A^+ \longrightarrow B^+ \quad + \quad C$$
accelerated $\quad$ detected $\quad$ neutral

The apparent mass ($M*$) observed on the spectrum is related to the masses of A^+ and B^+ by the relationship

$$M* \approx \frac{M_B{}^2}{M_A}$$

The precursor ion (A^+) is sometimes known as the parent ion—this should not be confused with the molecular ion (q.v.) which produces the parent peak (q.v.) on the mass spectrum.

The calculation of the mass/charge values for the precursor ion and the detected ion from the above formula has been greatly facilitated by publication of a list of metastable transitions[109].

Microcells (i.r.)
For micro-scale infrared spectroscopy special microcells are prepared by drilling a small cavity in a solid block of sodium chloride or potassium bromide[110]. By this means it is possible to prepare a cell with a path length of < 5 mm possessing an internal volume of about 0·2 µl. Silver chloride has also been used for this purpose.

An alternative type of microcell[111] uses small silver chloride windows at the end of a silver or Teflon tube with a capacity of 30 µl.

Micrometre µm
The recommended SI unit (q.v.) to take the place of the micron (μ)

$$1 \text{ µm} = 1 \times 10^{-6} \text{ m} = 1 \times 10^{-4} \text{ cm}$$

Micron
see Micrometre

Microprobe (em.)
see Laser microprobe

Microwave powered sources (a.s.)
see Electrodeless discharge tubes

Microwaves
The microwave region of the electromagnetic spectrum (q.v.) covers the wavelength range between 1 mm and 1 m. This apparent misnomer, as

regards spectroscopy, is because it is the micro- (or short)-wave region for the purpose of radio engineers.

Microwave spectroscopy
Transitions between different rotational energy levels of the same vibrational and electronic states are studied by the use of microwaves. Simple symmetric molecules such as CCl_4 do not give microwave spectra as it requires the existence of a permanent dipole moment in the molecule.

The microwave region employed is that between 1 mm and 30 cm (1000 MHz–300 GHz) and necessitates the use of klystron oscillators and waveguides (q.v.). The absorption cell for these studies is a piece of waveguide ten feet long sealed at each end with mica windows[112].

Millimicron
see Nanometre

Molar absorption coefficient
The currently recommended term to take the place of the molar extinction coefficient (q.v.).

Molar absorptivity
A non-recommended term for molar extinction coefficient (q.v.).

Molar decadic extinction coefficient
An uncommon expression employed with reference to the molar extinction coefficient (q.v.) expressed as a logarithmic value to the base ten, i.e. $\log_{10}\varepsilon$.

Molar extinction coefficient ε (i.r., u.v.)
This corresponds to the absorbance (q.v.) for a molar concentration of the material with a path length of 1 cm, determined at a specified wavelength. Under defined conditions of solvent, pH and temperature the molar extinction coefficient for a particular compound is a constant at the specified wavelength. The value of the molar extinction coefficient is obtained from the equation

$$\varepsilon = \frac{A}{cl}$$

Many different expressions have been suggested in place of molar extinction coefficient, such as molar absorptivity, but so far none has met with general acceptance. More recently the expression molar absorption coefficient has been accepted by a number of international bodies[2] and will probably come into general use over the next few years.

Molecular ion (m.s.)
Removal of an electron from a molecule by electron bombardment in the ion source produces the molecular ion of the species; this is detected at a mass/charge ratio that corresponds to the molecular weight of the molecule. The peak obtained from the molecular ions on the mass spectrum is known as the parent peak (q.v.) and is normally indicated by the letter P on the bar graph (q.v.).

Molecular leak (m.s.)
To prevent the vacuum in a mass spectrometer from being destroyed by too rapid a flow of sample and to ensure that the sample in the ionization chamber is representative of the sample in the reservoir it is slowly bled from the reservoir to the ionization chamber through a small adjustable orifice known as a 'leak'. By this means the ionization chamber is kept at a pressure of 10^{-5} torr or less. A wide variety of leaks have been used including porcelain rods, glass diaphragms, quartz tubes and capillary tubes.

Molecular spectra (i.r., u.v.)
An inclusive expression referring to spectra arising as a result of transitions in molecules. This includes electronic spectra (q.v.), studied in the ultra-violet/visible region, and vibrational or rotational spectra studied in the infrared region (q.v.).

Monochromatic radiation
Originally applied to visible light this literally means 'one colour'. It is now applied to any electromagnetic radiation in which the waves all have the same wavelength.

Monochromator
The purpose of the monochromator is to select electromagnetic radiation (q.v.) of a single frequency from a beam of radiation covering a wide range. This is achieved by employing the dispersion properties of either a prism

(q.v.) or a grating (q.v.). Some instruments may use both of these in combination, as in the double monochromator (q.v.), or separately in special mountings such as the Littrow mounting (q.v.).

Mössbauer spectroscopy

Mössbauer[113] found that in solid crystalline media the absorption or emission of γ radiation by nuclei occurred without the loss of recoil energy. This enabled nuclear energy levels to be studied. Conditions employed for the study require the γ-ray source to move relative to the absorbing species so that the Doppler effect (q.v.) produced adds energy to the system[115].

Mössbauer (or γ-resonance nuclear fluorescence) spectroscopy has many applications in qualitative and structural analysis[115] and the effect has been observed with 42 elements[116]; its main use, however, is in the study of iron and tin compounds.

Mulls (i.r.)

One method of obtaining infrared spectra from solid materials is to grind the powdered material with a liquid specially chosen to absorb only at unimportant sections of the spectrum. A fine dispersion of the solid in the mulling agent is produced which is then squeezed into a thin film between potassium bromide plates and placed in the infrared beam of the spectrometer. The most common mulling agent is liquid paraffin sold under the trade name Nujol (q.v.); and to obtain the spectrum in the region covered by the Nujol absorptions it is necessary to run a second mull prepared in a different liquid possessing no C–H bonds. Hexachlorobutadiene or Fluorolube (q.v.) are used for this purpose.

Only small quantities of material are required to make a mull, about 3 to 4 mg of the solid being ground with two or three drops of the mulling agent in an agate pestle and mortar.

Multi-centre fragmentation (m.s.)

Electron bombardment of a molecule in the ion source may lead to cleavage of several bonds, simultaneously producing a number of fragmentation ions, each of which can undergo further elimination and rearrangement processes. Such a result is known as a multi-centre fragmentation.

Multiple quantum transitions (n.m.r.)

see Combination lines

Multiple resonance (n.m.r.)

This is the term given to the application of two (double resonance) or more radio frequencies adjusted to enable several groups of nuclei to absorb energy at the same magnetic field strength. This leads to the collapse of the normal spin–spin coupling (q.v.) multiplicities for the irradiated nuclei and results in more simple spectra[117]. It is of particular value in structural determination of complicated molecules[118]. Two developments of the multiple resonance technique are INDOR (q.v.) and tickling (q.v.).

Figure 29. Multiple resonance. Spectra of n-propyl bromide, $CH_3CH_2CH_2Br$: (a) normal spectrum, showing spin–spin splitting; (b) effect of irradiating at frequency of the β-CH_2 group: α-CH_2 and CH_3 are collapsed to single lines; (c) effect of irradiating at frequency of CH_3 group: β-CH_2 becomes a triplet, α-CH_2 is unaffected. In each case the large arrow indicates the point of irradiation, and the spectra are frequency-swept ones

Multiplets (n.m.r.)

Spin–spin coupling (q.v.) between nuclei leads to simple n.m.r. absorption peaks being split into a number of smaller peaks. The nature of the multiplets produced is an indication of the number of coupling nuclei, and in the case of first-order spectra of protons can be predicted from the Pascal triangle (q.v.). The formation of multiplets occurs as a result of coupling between nuclei possessing different spins as well as between nuclei possessing identical spins.

The multiplicity of any absorption is established by the neighbouring nuclei. For protons it has been determined that n magnetically equivalent protons will give rise to a multiplicity of $n + 1$. The general equation applicable to any coupling nuclei is that n equivalent nuclei possessing a spin I will produce a multiplicity of $2nI + 1$.

see also Coupling constant

Multiplicity (pl.)

see Triplet state

Multiply charged ions (m.s.)

Ions produced in a mass spectrometer may carry more than one positive charge; these multiply charged ions are detected as a fraction of their true mass value as the spectrometer is actually measuring the mass/charge ratio. Thus doubly charged ions occur at half the true mass value and triply charged ions at one-third the true value. Such ions arise most readily with unsaturated organic compounds.

N

Nanometre nm

Under the scheme of SI units (q.v.) the nanometre has superseded the former expression millimicron (mμ). This dimension is used particularly for the ultraviolet/visible region in the range below 800 nm.

$$1 \text{ nm} = 10^{-9} \text{ m} = 10\text{Å}$$

Near-infrared region

see Infrared spectra

Nebulizers (a.s.)

Production of aerosols for atomic absorption spectroscopy is usually carried out by pneumatic devices called nebulizers (the word atomizer should not be used in this sense)[119]. The sample to be nebulized is drawn up a capillary either by the action of a current of air across the top of the capillary or by the passage of oxygen through a capillary concentric with the sample capillary. A high-pressure gas flow is necessary to produce the fine aerosol that is fed into the flame. Droplet sizes range from 1 to 50 µm and only about 10% of the sample actually reaches the flame[120].

Figure 30. Nebulizer

Negatively charged ions (m.s.)

Although mass spectrometers are normally used to examine positive ions it is possible to investigate the nature of any negatively charged ions formed by the ionization process by reversing the electric and magnetic fields in the source and the mass analyser. Negative ions occur most readily with elements possessing high electron affinities as the negative ions are frequently formed by electron capture processes. Spectra obtained from negative ions are weaker than are those from positive ions.

Negatron

see Electron

Nernst glower (i.r.)

This is one of the four types of source of infrared radiation used in spectrometers. It consists of a rod or hollow tube made from zirconium and thorium oxides[121] that glows when heated electrically to about 1800 °C. Other rare earth oxides may also be used in its formation. Because it is virtually a non-conductor at low temperatures it has to be preheated to 800 °C before further raising of the temperature can occur from the passage of electricity through the rod.

For most purposes the Nernst glower is about 3 cm long and 2 to 3 mm in diameter with platinum electrodes attached to each end.

cf. Globar; Nichrome source; Opperman source

Neutral fragments (m.s.)
In the formation of positive ions in mass spectrometry other ions and molecular fragments are also formed. Some of these carry no charge at all and cannot be resolved by the spectrometer. The nature of the neutral fragments can only be inferred from the positive ions that are formed and from the existence of metastable ions (q.v.).

Nichrome source (i.r.)
Basically a nickel and chromium alloy wire, this source can be unsupported or wound on a ceramic support. The wire itself radiates sufficient light of infrared frequency for it to have been widely used in infrared spectrophotometers.

cf. Globar; Nernst glower; Opperman source

Nier–Johnson mass analyser (m.s.)
Unlike the Mattauch–Herzog mass analyser (q.v.) this particular system uses electric and magnetic analysers both of 90° and deflecting the ions in the same direction. All ions are brought to a single focal point by varying either the accelerating voltage or the magnetic field.

Nitrogen rule (m.s.)
A substance containing an odd number of nitrogen atoms will have a molecular ion with an uneven mass number if the only other elements present are carbon, hydrogen, oxygen, sulphur or halogens. Similarly a molecule of even numbered molecular weight contains either no nitrogen or an even number of nitrogen atoms.

Non-bonding electrons
Electrons in the outer orbits of an atom in a molecule which are not involved in bond formation are known as non-bonding electrons. Such
electrons are easily removed by the electron bombardment in the mass
spectrometer ion source and play a major role in leading to fragmentation
and rearrangement of ions. Electrons in this classification include the
electrons on oxygen atoms in carbonyl groups:

$$> C = \ddot{\underset{\cdot\cdot}{O}}$$

Normal distribution
> *see* Gaussian distribution

Nuclear angular precession frequency ω_N (n.m.r.)
The angular frequency for nuclear precession is related to the magnetogyric
ratio and the applied field by the following equation:

$$\omega_N = \frac{geB}{2m_p} = \gamma_B$$

> cf. Larmor frequency

Nuclear g factor (n.m.r.)
The nuclear g factor is a dimensionless quantity characteristic of the
nucleus being studied and calculated from the equation

$$g = 1 + \frac{J(J+1) + S(S+1) - L(L+1)}{2J(J+1)}$$

It relates the magnetic moment of the particle and the angular momentum
according to the relationship

$$\mu = \frac{geh}{4\pi m_p c} \{I(I+1)\}^{1/2} = g\mu_N \{I(I+1)\}^{1/2}$$

For most nuclei g varies between 0·1 and 6. This differs from the Landé
factor (q.v.) for electrons.

101

Nuclear magnetic resonance spectroscopy

This realm of spectroscopy is concerned with the study of the interaction of energy with atomic nuclei. Most atomic nuclei possess a nuclear spin which can have a number of energy states depending upon the value of the nuclear spin quantum number (q.v.) for the nucleus. Nuclear magnetic resonance spectroscopy measures the energy necessary to bring about transitions between these energy levels by subjecting the nuclei to a powerful magnetic field and simultaneously irradiating it with a radio-frequency source[122]. In the case of protons suitable conditions for resonance occur with the use of a field of 1·4 tesla and a radio frequency of about 60 MHz.

see also Coupling constant; Spin–spin coupling

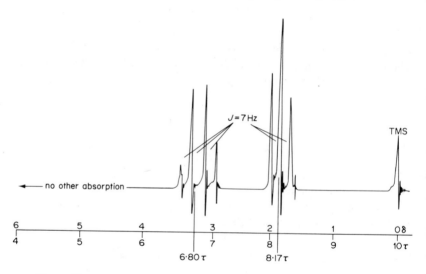

Figure 31. n.m.r. spectrum. Illustrating coupling between a methyl group (8·17τ) and a methylene group (6·80τ)

Nuclear magneton μ_N (n.m.r.)

This is the unit for the measurement of nuclear magnetic moments and has the value of $5\cdot050\,951 \times 10^{-27}\ \mathrm{J\,T^{-1}}$.

$$\mu_N = \frac{m_e}{m_p}\mu_B = \frac{eh}{4\pi m_p}$$

Nuclear quadrupole moment Q

Nuclei with spin quantum numbers greater than $\frac{1}{2}$ have quadrupole moments due to the non-uniform distribution of the electric charge throughout the nucleus. Nuclear quadrupole resonance spectroscopy is used to study the transitions that can occur between the energy states that exist owing to this lack of symmetry[123]. Interaction with nuclear quadrupole moments leads to line broadening in n.m.r. spectra; this occurs particularly in the study of proton spectra when the protons are attached to nitrogen atoms $(I = 1)$.

Nuclear quadrupole resonance

Owing to the existence of the nuclear quadrupole moment (q.v.) identical nuclei in different chemical compounds will exist at different energy levels. As a result they will give resonance peaks at different frequencies and this can serve as a guide to the nature of the bonding and the molecular structure. The effect is studied in nuclear quadrupole resonance spectroscopy[124], the transitions occurring between 10^6 and 10^9 Hz in an oscillating magnetic field.

Nuclear satellite signals (n.m.r.)

Owing to the presence of 1% ^{13}C in naturally occurring carbon and its compounds all resonance spectra of protons attached to carbon atoms show small additional peaks due to spin–spin coupling (q.v.) between the hydrogen nuclei and the ^{13}C nuclei. These satellite signals are found on either side of the normal proton absorptions and the coupling constant J_{CH} is about 200 Hz. These satellite signals should not be confused with spinning side bands (q.v.); their presence can be emphasized and useful information obtained by expanding the normal n.m.r. signals off-scale.

Nuclear screening constant σ (n.m.r.)

The local magnetic field around a nucleus situated in the magnetic field of an n.m.r. spectrometer is usually less than the applied external field and is given by the equation

$$H_{local} = (1 - \sigma)H_0$$

where σ is the nuclear screening constant. This is the total of a number of diamagnetic (q.v.) and paramagnetic (q.v.) effects involving the circulation

103

of electrons around the nucleus or nuclei studied and the production of small magnetic fields in opposition to the main field.

Nuclear spin (n.m.r.)
The nuclear spin of magnetic nuclei results in the magnetic moment (q.v.); such nuclei possess a spin quantum number (q.v.) that determines the number of orientations that the spinning nucleus may occupy in the presence of an external magnetic field. Non-magnetic nuclei do not exhibit nuclear spin.

Nuclear spin quantum number I (n.m.r.)
see Spin quantum number

Nuclear spin temperature T_S (n.m.r.)
This is an expression used to describe the number of nuclei in the different spin states. For protons

$$T_s = \frac{2\mu H}{k \ln(n_+/n_-)}$$

where n_+ and n_- are the number of nuclei in the upper and lower states respectively.

The spin temperature has a positive value when the population in the lower state exceeds that in the upper state.

Nujol (i.r.)
Nujol is a trade name for a high-boiling petroleum fraction used as a mulling medium in the study of solids by infrared spectroscopy. Being a mixture of hydrocarbons the only absorptions present are those due to C–C and C–H bonds occurring in four short regions: 3000–2700 cm^{-1} (3·3–3·6 μm), 1470–1410 cm^{-1} (6·8–7·1 μm), 1380–1350 cm^{-1} (7·3–7·4 μm) and 730–710 cm^{-1} (13·7–14·1 μm).

see also Mulls

O

Opperman source (i.r.)

A ceramic (alkali based) tube with an internal noble metal heater. This type of source needs no preheating and emits powerfully at infrared frequencies straight from switch-on.

Commercially it is one of the most widely used sources.

cf. Globar; Nernst glower; Nichrome source

Optical comb

see Attenuator

Optical density

This term has been superseded by absorbance (q.v.).

Optical glass

Two main groups of optical glass are used; these are crown glass with a refractive index ≈ 1.52 and flint glass with a refractive index of about 1.65. The two types of glass are frequently used together to produce achromatic systems (q.v.).

Optical null principle (i.r.)

The basis of this principle is the use of a servo operated attenuator. Typically, absorption of energy in the sample beam of a double beam system is matched, through the action of a servomotor, by the movement of an attenuator (q.v.) in the reference beam. The servo circuits are designed to drive the attenuator to the 'matched' position where there is 'null' difference between the energy transmitted by the two beams. The recorder pen follows the movement of the attenuator, thus providing the spectra.

Optical rotary dispersion (u.v.)

Optical rotary dispersion is the study of the variation of the angle of polarization for optically active materials with the change in wavelength. The effect is normally studied over the 200–700 nm spectral range using light monochromated from a xenon light source. It is used to differentiate

105

between structures with different conformations and to establish the position of substituents in large molecules such as steroids[125].

Ordinate

This is the name given to the vertical axis in a set of two-dimensional coordinates. Usually this is referred to as the Y axis, so that the ordinate of any point in the plane of the two axes forming the coordinates is the value at the place on the Y axis at which a horizontal line from the point meets that axis.

see also Abscissa

Overhauser effect (e.s.r., n.m.r.)

Nuclear electron double resonance (the Overhauser effect) is the study of nuclear resonance absorption signals whilst the sample is simultaneously irradiated at an electron resonance. The n.m.r. absorption signals for the spinning nuclei can be substantially enhanced by this irradiation if saturation of the associated spinning electrons is obtained. This is because the equilibrium of the coupling between the spinning electrons and the spinning nuclei is altered and an increased population difference between the nuclear energy levels is produced[126].

The reverse effect to the Overhauser effect[127] is ENDOR (q.v.). Although the Overhauser effect is of particular value for nuclear–electron spin interactions, it has also been used for the study of nuclear–nuclear spin interactions.

Overtones (i.r.)

The term overtone is used in a general sense to apply to any multiple of a given fundamental frequency v, i.e. $2v$, $3v$, etc. In infrared spectroscopy most overtones are found in the near-infrared region below 2·5 µm (beyond 4000 cm^{-1}). Such absorptions are much weaker than are the main absorption bands, but may still be of spectroscopic interest. Aromatic compounds, for example, show overtone absorptions in the 2000–1667 cm^{-1} (5–6 µm) region which are characteristic for the type of aromatic substitution[128].

P

Parallel vibration (i.r.)

A vibration of a molecule leading to a change in dipole moment in a direction parallel to the symmetry axis. Such a vibration is infrared active.

cf. Perpendicular vibration

Paramagnetic broadening (n.m.r.)

One cause of the broadening of n.m.r. absorption peaks can be the presence of paramagnetic species in the sample under investigation. These have the effect of reducing the longitudinal (q.v.) relaxation time due to the much greater magnetic field associated with the paramagnetic substances. Dissolved oxygen is frequently a cause of paramagnetic broadening and free radicals can also have this effect.

Paramagnetism

Paramagnetism is a property of substances arising from the unbalanced spin of electrons around nuclei in molecules possessing unpaired electrons. Within an applied magnetic field the atoms tend to orientate themselves in the direction of the field and possess a positive magnetic susceptibility[129]. The degree of orientation parallel to the applied field increases with the strength of the field.

Parent peak (m.s.)

The molecular ion (q.v.) formed by loss of a single electron from the molecule gives rise to the peak on the mass spectrum corresponding to the molecular weight. This peak is usually referred to as the parent peak and is indicated on the bar graph (q.v.) by the letter P. Other peaks are normally detected at 1 and 2 mass units greater than this; these are referred to as the $P + 1$ and $P + 2$ peaks. They arise owing to the presence of heavy isotopes in the molecules.

N.B. The term parent ion is sometimes used to refer to the precursor ion in a metastable transition (*see* Metastable ions).

see also Isotopic abundance

107

Parts per million (n.m.r.)

This is a dimensionless scale used on n.m.r. spectra in order that chemical shift positions relative to a standard can be expressed independently from the field strength of the instrument employed.

For a particular absorption the value in p.p.m. is given by

$$\delta = \frac{(H_{ref} - H_{sample}) \, 10^6}{H_{ref}}$$

In proton spectra δ values usually increase in a downfield direction away from the TMS reference (q.v.) signal; most absorption values lie between 0 and 10δ. Another system of numbering that refers specifically to TMS and protons is the τ scale, this numbers in the reverse direction so that $\tau = 10 - \delta$.

Figure 32. Parts per million. Proton n.m.r. spectrum of chloroform showing relationship between δ and τ parts per million and instrument frequency

see also Nuclear magnetic resonance spectroscopy

Pascal Pa

see Pressure, units

Pascal constants (n.m.r.)

In calculations of magnetic moments it is necessary to compensate for any contributing diamagnetic effects. The molar diamagnetic susceptibility (χ_m) is estimated from the sum of the atomic contributions, the values of which are known as Pascal constants[130].

108

Pascal triangle (e.s.r., n.m.r.)

In the binomial series (q.v.), $(x + y)^n$, successive coefficients can be obtained by forming a triangle of numbers such that a number in a line is obtained from the sum of the two numbers above it in the preceding line. In its simplest form the triangle serves to show the relative sizes of the peaks in multiplicities in first-order e.s.r. and n.m.r. spectra for nuclei in which $I = \frac{1}{2}$; as shown in table 4 below.

Table 4

Number of coupling nuclei	Ratio of multiplicity peak heights
0	1
1	1　1
2	1　2　1
3	1　3　3　1
4	1　4　6　4　1
5	1　5　10　10　5　1
6	1　6　15　20　15　6　1

Similar triangles have been developed for $I = 1$ and $I = \frac{3}{2}$.

Perfluorokerosene (m.s.)

Because of the multiplicity of fragment ions obtainable from this fluorinated hydrocarbon it is used extensively as a standard for peak assignment in mass spectra. In some cases it is employed as an internal standard to produce an overlapping spectrum with the other material under examination. It is also used as a mulling agent, under the name Fluorolube (q.v.), for infrared spectra.

Permeability μ

The permeability of a body is the ratio of the magnetic flux density (q.v.) passing through that body to the flux density of the magnetic field in the absence of the body.

$$\mu = \frac{B}{H}$$

It is measured in henry per metre, where $1\ H\ m^{-1} = 1\ m\ kg\ s^{-2}\ A^{-2}$.

Perpendicular vibration (i.r.)

A vibration of a molecule leading to a change in dipole moment in a direction perpendicular to the symmetry axis. Such a vibration will be infrared active.

cf. Parallel vibration

Phosphorescence (pl.)

Transitions from triplet states (q.v.) to the ground electronic state give rise to phosphorescent emissions. The lifetime of the triplet state is typically milliseconds but can be as long as ten seconds. Because of this long lifetime molecules in the triplet state may lose their energy by other deactivation processes. Phosphorescence is, therefore, best observed in solid solution at low temperature with the exclusion of oxygen.

Photocell

This is a general term for any cell made from photo-sensitive materials such that incident radiation causes the release of electrons that can be conducted away, amplified and recorded. Typical substances employed for this purpose are cadmium sulphide, lead sulphide and germanium. Lead sulphide has been of particular value in the development of the photoelectric infrared detectors and cadmium sulphide and selenide have been similarly used for visible light.

Photoelectric infrared detectors (i.r.)

Also known as lead sulphide conductive cells these detectors are suitable for a limited region of the near- and middle-infrared spectrum between 1 and 6 μm. They exhibit an increase in conductivity when infrared radiation is incident upon the surface, composed of lead sulphide, selenide or telluride[131].

The detector consists of a 0·1 μm layer of the lead compound upon glass forming a semiconductor system which becomes a conducting system owing to the absorption of infrared radiation. The resistance of the detector decreases with the increase in intensity of the incident radiation.

Photoelectron spectroscopy

The liberation of electrons from different orbits of atoms requires a quantity of energy that depends upon the nature of the electron orbit. Study of these ionization energies (q.v.) is most readily carried out by subjecting the atoms to a beam of photons, and this is known as photoelectron spectroscopy. Ultraviolet radiation and x-rays are both used for this purpose. The former is used for low-energy investigations of outer orbits, whilst the latter are more suitable for high-energy studies of inner core electrons.

Photoemissive tube (u.v.)

This detector consists of a photoemissive cathode, which emits electrons when radiation is incident upon its surface, and an anode collector enclosed in a glass jacket. Most commonly the cathode consists of caesium oxide, caesium, silver oxide and silver in a composite layer on a nickel base. Electrons released from the cathode due to incident radiation pass to the anode and the signal is amplified. Most photoemissive tubes give a good response over a range of about 300 nm.

Photo-ionization source (m.s.)

Sample ionization for mass spectrometry can be achieved by irradiating the sample with ultraviolet light. The ultraviolet radiation source is separated from the ionization chamber by a lithium fluoride window. The method is limited to the formation of molecular ions and fragments formed by energies less than the 11·8 eV effective power from the light source used.

Photoluminescence (pl.)

A general term used for the irregular re-emission of radiation from a molecule which has absorbed electromagnetic radiation (q.v.) from the infrared, visible or ultraviolet regions. It includes both fluorescence (q.v.) and phosphorescence (q.v.). Over a time period the amount of re-emitted radiation is equal in all directions.

Photometer

In traditional terms the word 'photometer' is applied to any instrument used to measure the total amount of radiant energy absorbed or transmitted by a sample. A simple photometer does not, therefore, include a mono-chromator (q.v.) or a system for scanning a spectral range.

see also Spectrophotometer

111

Photomultiplier (a.s., u.v.)
This is a sensitive, rapidly responding detector system in which photo-electrons produced by radiation falling on a cathode are amplified by a cascade process (q.v.). Each electron from the cathode produces two or more electrons by impact with the surface of a dynode plate (q.v.). These are amplified in turn by impact on further dynode plates arranged in series (of which there may be ten or more). Because of the substantial amplification factor the photomultiplier is particularly useful in detecting signals of weak intensity.

Very sensitive photomultipliers were used in the ultraviolet spectrometers in the *Mariner 6* and *7* spacecrafts sent to Mars[132] in 1969. Caesium iodide was used as a photocathode for 110 to 210 nm and a bialkali metal for 190 to 430 nm.

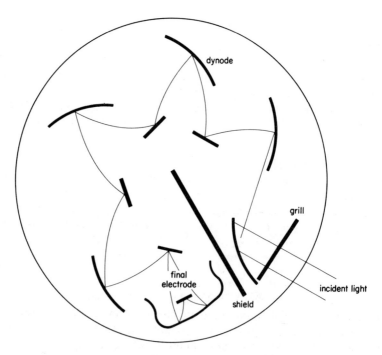

Figure 33. Cascade process in a photomultiplier

Photons
Electromagnetic energy is produced in discrete small quantities, 'quanta', called photons. Photons produced at a particular frequency possess the same energy, but the amount of energy in a photon depends upon its frequency of radiation.

see Planck constant

Phototube

see Photoemissive tube

Photovoltaic cell (u.v.)

see Barrier layer cell

Planck constant h
The Planck constant is the proportionality constant in the equation

$$E = h\nu$$

derived for the statement of the Planck law that energy transfers occur with radiation composed of quanta of energy related to the frequency of the corresponding radiation.

The value of h is $6 \cdot 626\ 196 \times 10^{-34}$ J s.

It is sometimes used in the form h bar where

$$\hbar = \frac{h}{2\pi} = 1 \cdot 054\ 592 \times 10^{-34} \text{ J s}$$

It is also used as $h/2e = 2 \cdot 067\ 854 \times 10^{-16}$ J s C^{-1}.

Planck law of radiation
The intensity of radiation from a black body at a particular wavelength (the spectral radiant energy density) is given by

$$w_\lambda = \frac{8\pi h c \lambda^{-5}}{e^{hc/kT\lambda} - 1}$$

All other equations concerning black-body radiation can be derived from the Planck equation.

see also Rayleigh and Jeans law; Stefan–Boltzmann law;
Wien laws

Plane of symmetry (i.r.)

A plane of symmetry is said to exist in a molecule if it is possible to draw a plane through the molecule in such a way that the half of the molecule on one side is a mirror image of the half on the other side.

see also Axis of symmetry; Centre of symmetry

Plasma jet (or torch) (a.s.)

The plasma torch is produced by using radio-frequency excited discharges in inert gases at atmospheric pressures.

The sample is introduced as a mist with nitrogen or argon carrier gas and a radio-frequency signal is fed by a waveguide (q.v.) to the coaxial jet terminating in a molybdenum tip. The tube and resulting jet are enclosed in an open quartz jacket[133]. Results are often superior to flame techniques[134].

Pneumatic cell (i.r.)

Of the various detectors available for infrared radiation this is the most sensitive that has so far been developed[135]. The incident radiation causes the expansion of a small volume of gas contained in a closed cell. The expansion displaces a small mirror and reduces the amount of light reflected onto a photocell through a line grid[136]. The change in light intensity as a result of this displacement is proportional to the incident infrared radiation and is measured and recorded. The detector has been of special application in far-infrared spectrometers.

cf. Bolometer; Thermocouple

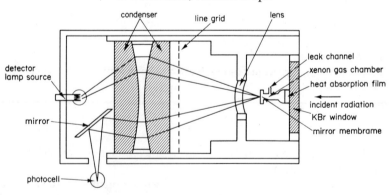

Figure 34. Pneumatic cell—Golay detector

Polarizers

The examination of samples under polarized infrared radiation is of particular interest in the study of crystals and polymers. Several types of polarizers are made for this purpose. Stacks of cellulose lacquer films coated with selenium have been employed[137], which will produce 99·8% polarization when inclined to the incident beam at the Brewster angle (q.v.). Silver chloride plates 0·005 cm thick have also been employed in this way[138].

Wire grid polarizers[139] are now the most commonly used. They consist of a network of fine parallel metal wires deposited on an infrared-transparent substrate. The metal is usually gold, whilst the substrate can be silver bromide (for 2·5 to 40 μm, with 2880 lines mm^{-1}), polyethylene (for > 15 μm, with 640 lines mm^{-1})[140], or Irtran-2 and Irtran-4 (q.v.)[141].

Polychromatic radiation

Although literally meaning 'many coloured' the expression is used in connection with any electromagnetic radiation consisting of a mixture of wavelengths. Most sources in spectroscopy give polychromatic radiation which must be passed through a monochromator (q.v.) to obtain a selected wavelength or narrow band required for the spectroscopic examination.

Polystyrene

see Calibration peaks

Population inversion (n.m.r., r.s.)

This is the name given to a situation in which the number of active species occupying a particular energy state is greater than that predicted by the Boltzmann ratio (q.v.). This is of special consideration in lasers (q.v.) in which excited states of extended lifetimes are produced and population inversions deliberately created.

In n.m.r. spectroscopy population inversions occur if relaxation (q.v.) from the higher nuclear energy state to the lower energy state is too slow.

Positron

see Electron

Precession (n.m.r.)

Nuclei possessing magnetic moments act as if they are small spinning magnets and will rotate when under the influence of an applied magnetic field. This motion is known as precession and takes place at a rate defined by the Larmor frequency (q.v.). The precession axis of the spinning nucleus describes a circle at right angles to the direction of the applied field.

Pressed discs (i.r.)

One method of obtaining infrared spectra from solids is by grinding and compressing a small quantity (*ca.* 2 mg) of sample with dry potassium bromide or potassium chloride (*ca.* 200 mg) under a pressure of 10 to 15 ton in^{-2} (154 to 231 M N m^{-2}). This method of sampling has the advantage that the solid supports employed do not absorb between 4000 and 700 cm^{-1}. The discs produced by this method measure about 1 cm in diameter and 1 to 2 mm in thickness and are normally reasonably transparent if the mixture has been adequately mixed and ground together.

Pressure broadening (a.s., em.)

Broadening of absorption and emission lines in atomic spectra that occurs as a result of collisions between excited atoms and other atoms and molecules in the flame is called pressure broadening. This effect is partially overcome in atomic absorption spectroscopy by the use of low pressures in electrodeless discharge tubes (q.v.) and hollow cathode lamps (q.v.).

cf. Doppler broadening

Pressure, units (m.s.)

The recommended SI unit (q.v.) for pressure is the pascal (Pa) measured in kg m^{-1} s^{-2} = N m^{-2} = J m^{-3}.

It has been suggested that although the bar is a multiple of the pascal its use should be progressively abandoned.

$$1 \text{ bar} = 10^5 \text{ Pa}$$

It has also been recommended that the use of the torr and millimetres of mercury should be discontinued.

$$1 \text{ torr} \approx 1 \text{ mmHg} \approx 133 \cdot 322 \text{ Pa}$$

Primary filter (pl.)

The primary filter system is used to select the appropriate wavelength from the light source employed in the filter fluorimeter. The filter (q.v.) used may be of special glass or a chemical solution[142]. For the mercury arc source cobalt sulphate solution may be used to isolate the 253·7 nm line and a glass filter to obtain the 334·1 nm line.

Prisms, infrared

The prisms used for dispersion in infrared spectrometers are of many types as no prism is completely suited for the entire infrared region. Most general purpose prism instruments employ a sodium chloride prism, but operation in the far infrared necessitates the use of other materials. The following table gives the operating ranges for the most common prism materials.

see also Gratings

Table 5

Material	Frequency range/cm^{-1}	Wavelength range/μm
caesium iodide	5000–200	2·0–50·0
sodium chloride	5000–650	2·0–15·4
KRS-5	5000–1300	2·0– 7·7
calcium fluoride	4500–1300	2·2– 7·7
lithium fluoride	4500–1700	2·5– 5·9
potassium bromide	1100–285	9·1–35·0

Prisms, ultraviolet

Although glass is an admirable material for prisms for studying visible spectra it is unsuitable for the ultraviolet region. For this reason most modern general-purpose prism ultraviolet spectrometers employ a quartz or silica prism capable of operating over a wider spectral range. The normal operating limits are shown below.

Table 6

Material	Useful range/nm
glass	350–1000
quartz	200–1000

Probes (m.s.)

see Direct insertion probes

Probes (n.m.r.)

This is the name given to the part of the n.m.r. spectrometer which is situated between the pole faces of the magnet. It includes the sample

117

chamber which enables the sample tube to be positioned precisely with respect to the irradiation and detection coils contained in the probe. The probe itself has to be symmetrically positioned in the homogeneous portion of the magnetic field of the instrument. Because it is virtually a self-contained section a single n.m.r. instrument may be supplied with several interchangeable probes each suitable for the study of a different element.

Pulsed laser (r.s.)

see Laser

Pulsed mode (m.s.)
Operation of a pulsed-mode time-of-flight mass spectrometer involves ionization of the sample by short pulses of the electron beam (250 ns). The positive ions formed are then released into the accelerating region by a negative pulse (300 V) lasting 2·5 μs on the ion focus grid.

cf. Continuous mode

Pulse method (n.m.r.)
Longitudinal and transverse relaxation times (q.v.) can be determined by pulse experiments in which the n.m.r. spectrum is studied by means of short bursts (short compared with T_1 and T_2) of radio-frequency energy at the resonance energy. The application of correctly timed amounts of energy leads to a nuclear signal (spin echo) whilst no radio-frequency energy is applied. The method has also been used to measure coupling constants (q.v.).

Q

Quadrupole broadening (n.m.r.)
The width of an n.m.r. absorption peak is broadened if there is a decrease in the relaxation time (q.v.) as can be caused by the existence of a non-spherical charge distribution on other or the same nuclei (*see* Quadrupole moment). This is known as quadrupole broadening and occurs in the presence of nuclei in which $I > \frac{1}{2}$ which possess quadrupole moments.

This is the reason for the broad absorption signals obtained for protons attached to ^{14}N.

Quadrupole coupling (n.m.r.)

The interaction of two nuclei, one of which possesses a non-spherical charge distribution (*see* Quadrupole moment) is called quadrupole coupling. It leads to a broadening of the n.m.r. absorption signal of the other magnetic nucleus.

see also Quadrupole broadening

Quadrupole mass spectrometer (m.s.)

Mass spectra—up to a mass/charge ratio of 500—can be obtained by passing the ion beam along the central axis of four parallel quartz rods coated with platinum which are connected in pairs to radio-frequency and d.c. supplies. These voltages create a hyperbolic field between the rods and only one particular mass value can traverse the path between the rods for any specified combination of r.f. and d.c. voltages. Scanning of the mass range is carried out by varying the voltages. This system has the advantage that mass peaks are separated by a constant distance and do not crowd together at high mass values[143,144].

The quartz rods in the mass quadrupole measure about 1 cm in diameter and 20 cm long, operating with 3 MHz r.f. and 10 V d.c.

Figure 35. Quadrupole mass spectrometer

119

Quadrupole moment Q (n.m.r.)
Nuclei which have a spin quantum number (q.v.) $I > \frac{1}{2}$ possess electric quadrupole moments as a result of a non-spherical distribution of the charge in the nucleus. Nuclei in which $I = \frac{1}{2}$ cannot possess electric quadrupole moments. Those nuclei possessing quadrupole moments, such as ^{2}H, ^{11}B and ^{14}N, cause quadrupole broadening (q.v.) of n.m.r. absorption signals from other nuclei.

Quanta
see Photons

Quarter-wave plate
see Retardation plate

Quenching (pl.)
This is the process whereby fluorescence is decreased as a result of a change in pH of solution or by some added chemical that assists the excited molecules to transfer their excess energy before fluorescent emission can take place. Quenching as a result of impurities and added chemicals can be reduced by dilution of the fluorescent solution.

R

Radiant energy
This is energy which is transmitted by means of electromagnetic waves without involving the transfer of matter.

Radical ion (m.s.)
Removal of an electron from a molecule due to bombardment with electrons from the ion source leads to the formation of a positively charged radical ion. This radical ion (also known as the molecular ion) is detected on the mass spectrometer and recorded as the parent peak (q.v.).

$$R\!:\!R' \xrightarrow{\;-e\;} R\overset{+}{\cdot}R'$$
radical ion

Radio-frequency spark discharge source (m.s.)
> *see* Spark ionization source

Raies Ultimes (em.)
> *see* R.U.

Raman effect (r.s.)

Although originally predicted by Smekal[145] this effect was first examined by Raman[146] in 1928. He observed that a small proportion of radiation passing through a substance emerged with either an increase or a decrease in the frequency. This occurred because after being raised to an excited state some of the excited molecules returned to a higher or lower vibrational level in the ground electronic state. Raman transitions may also be vibrational–rotational or simply rotational[147] in nature. The lifetime of the Raman excited state is about 10^{-12} s and only about 1 in 10^6 molecules exhibit the effect at any particular moment.
> *see also* Anti-Stokes lines; Stokes lines

Raman spectroscopy

Modern Raman spectroscopy is carried out with lasers (q.v.) as the source of radiation[95]. The spectra obtained are complementary to normal infrared spectra and assist in the determination of molecular dimensions. The Raman lines are observed on either side of the monochromatic laser frequency and are referred to as Stokes (q.v.) and Anti-Stokes lines (q.v.). Visible light is normally employed for the purposes of excitation as the intensity of the resulting Raman lines is proportional to the fourth power of the frequency of the irradiation[148].
> *see also* Laser Raman spectroscopy

Figure 36. Raman spectrum of mesitylene

121

Rapid scanning spectrometers

A number of specially designed spectrometers have been developed that are capable of measuring spectra in fractions of a second. These are particularly suitable for studying combustions and rapid reactions in solution. The instruments employ a pneumatic cell detector (q.v.) with a cathode-ray oscilloscope and a rapidly moving Littrow mounting (q.v.).

Rayleigh and Jeans law

An attempt to develop an equation for black-body radiation using statistical mechanics was used by Rayleigh and Jeans. The equation they obtained agrees with experimental values at long wavelengths and at high temperatures and is given by

$$M\lambda = 2\pi hc^2\lambda^{-5}(\lambda T)$$

see also Planck law; Stefan–Boltzmann law; Wien laws

Rayleigh scattering (r.s.)

Some light passing through a transparent medium is scattered instead of following the main light path. In the case of elastic (Rayleigh) scattering there is no change in the wavelength of the scattered light. Most of the scattered radiation is in this category, but a small amount may undergo inelastic scattering giving rise to the Raman effect (q.v.). About 1 part in 10^3 of the incident light undergoes Rayleigh scattering and the amount of light scattered (I_θ) in a direction θ to the incident beam is given by

$$\frac{I_\theta r_s^2}{I_0} = \frac{8\pi^2\alpha^2}{\lambda^4}(1 + \cos^2\theta)$$

R bands (u.v.)

Absorption bands arising from $n \rightarrow \pi^*$ transitions are referred to as R bands (from the German radikalartig) according to the system of nomenclature used by Burawoy[13] and Braude[14]. Such transitions occur in auxochromes (q.v.) possessing non-bonding electrons.

see Bands (ultraviolet)

Reaction field theory (n.m.r.)

This is an attempt to explain the effect of solvents on chemical shifts (q.v.) in n.m.r. spectroscopy[149]. It concerns the effect of solvent dielectric constants and polar groups. The polar groups are said to set up 'reaction fields' in the solvent causing the electrons in the bonds to be redistributed, thus reinforcing the shielding (q.v.) or deshielding (q.v.) within the molecules.

Red shift (u.v.)
> *see* Bathochromic shift

Reflection
A beam of radiant energy is said to be reflected when its line of direction is changed along another single direction as a result of meeting a smooth polished surface. When reflection occurs the angle between the incident beam and the surface is identical with that between the reflected beam and the surface. Also the two beams and the normal at the point of incidence are in the same plane.

Reflectometer (i.r., u.v.)
Reflection spectra are obtained from the surfaces of samples fitted into reflectometer attachments for conventional spectrometers. This may be in the form of a diffuse reflectance unit such as that used in ultraviolet spectrometers for the study of papers, powders and tiles by comparison with a magnesium oxide standard. These give front-surface reflection spectra which are influenced by particle size. Reflectance spectra are also obtained by attenuated total reflectance (q.v.).

Refraction
When a beam of radiant energy passes from one medium into another of lesser or greater optical density it undergoes a change in direction known as refraction. The angle of incidence of the beam and the angle of refraction, relative to a perpendicular to the two surfaces at the point of incidence, are related by the equation

$$\frac{\text{sine } i}{\text{sine } r} = \frac{n'}{n}$$

where n and n' are the refractive indices of the two media. In those cases in which the incident ray passes through air n is taken as unity and the equation becomes

$$\frac{\text{sine } i}{\text{sine } r} = n'$$

As the value of n' varies with both temperature and wavelength it is usual

123

to indicate both of these; n_D^{20} means that the refractive index was determined at 20 °C using the yellow sodium D lines at 589·0 and 589·6 nm.

Relaxation (n.m.r.)

The process of change from a high nuclear energy level to a lower energy level is known as relaxation and may be of two types; longitudinal relaxation (q.v.) or transverse relaxation (q.v.). In solids or viscous liquids the relaxation time may be hours, but in non-viscous liquids relaxation times vary from 10^{-2} to 10^2 s. Where relaxation is slow compared with the excitation process saturation (q.v.) takes place.

Resolution—mass spectrometry

This is the ability of the mass analyser (q.v.) to separate two ions of mass M and $M + \Delta M$ from each other, the resolution being given by

$$R = \frac{M}{\Delta M}$$

Considerable confliction exists over the manner in which data on resolution is presented as in some cases this refers to peaks which are only just distinguishable from each other, as when there is 90% overlap (valley) which is poor resolution; whilst in other cases it may refer to 50% valley or 10% valley. These are illustrated in the figure below. Most responsible manufacturers now specify the resolution as the mass value at which the 10% valley is obtained. Using this definition most general-purpose mass spectrometers of the single-focusing type (q.v.) have resolution values below 2000, whilst double-focusing instruments have values greater than 10 000.

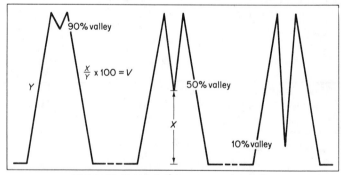

Figure 37. Resolution in mass spectrometers

Resolution—spectrophotometers
The ability of a monochromator to separate radiation of similar wavelengths is known as resolution and is given by the formula

$$R = \frac{\lambda}{\Delta\lambda}$$

when the two wavelengths λ and $\lambda + \Delta\lambda$ can just be differentiated from each other. Resolution can be improved by a narrow slit width and good dispersion.

The resolving power for a prism is

$$R = t\,\frac{\partial n}{\partial \lambda}$$

where t is the base width and $\partial n/\partial \lambda$ is known as the dispersive power of the prism.

High resolution in ultraviolet spectrophotometers is better than 0·2 nm at 250 nm.

Response time (i.r.)
The time required by the detector in a spectrophotometer to reach equilibrium when there is a change in the amount of radiant energy falling on its sensitive surface. For modern detectors this is less than 0·03 s.
cf. Time constant

Retardation plate
A phase difference is created between the ordinary and extraordinary rays of polarized light by passage of an incident ray through a retardation plate. The plates are formed from double-refracting materials cut parallel to the optic axis. The effect of a quarter-wave plate is to introduce a phase difference of 90° between the two emergent rays, and a half-wave plate introduces a phase difference of 180°.

Ring current effect (n.m.r.)
Aromatic protons are found to absorb at low field in n.m.r. spectra because of deshielding (q.v.) of the ring protons. The deshielding is attributed to the toroidal shape of the induced field due to the electron distribution above

125

and below the plane of the benzene ring. This is called the ring current effect and occurs with other unsaturated systems.

Ringing (n.m.r.)
The term is given to the exponentially decaying oscillations which are frequently observed with sharp n.m.r. absorption signals. These are particularly associated with the TMS (q.v.) reference peak. It occurs at the high-field end of any sharp peak if a rapid sweep of the spectrum is carried out from the low- to the high-field direction. A good symmetrical ringing oscillation on the TMS absorption is usually taken as an indication of an homogeneous magnetic field.

Rocking vibration (i.r.)
One of the forms of bending vibration (q.v.) in which the vibrational motion of the group is in the form of a rocking movement within the plane of the group.

Rotating sector mirror (i.r.)
A circular mirror with alternate segments cut away so that on rotation it will alternately reflect and pass any light directed to it. The system is frequently used in spectrophotometers when it is required to pass two beams along the same path in alternate pulses. In this application one of the beams comes from behind the rotating mirror and passes through when in line with the cut-away portions and follows the same path as the beam of incident light on the reflecting segments of the mirror.

Rotational spectra (i.r.)
Pure rotational spectra are found in the far-infrared region (q.v.) between 50 μm and 200 μm and in the microwave region (q.v.). They arise from the absorption of electromagnetic radiation and its total conversion to produce or change the molecular rotation. In the middle-infrared region rotational changes occur simultaneously with the vibrational changes (q.v.).

Rowland mounting (em.)
A slit, a grating and a photographic plate are arranged at the three points of a right-angled triangle in such a way that the hypotenuse of the triangle is the diameter of a circle passing through the three points. This arrange-

ment is used in some emission spectrographs in which the spectrum is scanned by moving both the grating and the photographic plate.

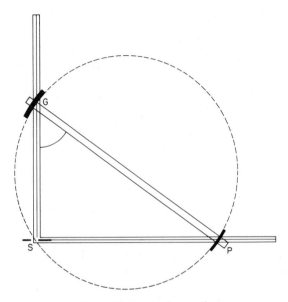

Figure 38. Rowland mounting

R.U. (em.)

Raies Ultimes are the most persistent lines in the emission spectrum of any element. They are the lines which are the last to disappear as the concentration of that element is progressively decreased. Because of this they are of great importance for detecting trace amounts of the particular element.

Specially manufactured R.U. powders are mixtures of substances employing concentrations that will only give the R.U. lines of the elements incorporated and are used as reference standards and for calibration purposes.

Rydberg constant R_∞

The Rydberg constant (now expressed in terms of waves per metre) was introduced as the constant required for the equation for the calculation of the atomic spectra (q.v.) series. It is calculated from the following relationship:

$$R_\infty = \frac{\mu_0{}^2 m_e e^4 c^3}{8h^3} = 1{\cdot}097\ 373\ 12 \times 10^7\ \text{m}^{-1}$$

In the formula for spectra of hydrogen and other light atoms and ions the value of R_∞ is modified by allowing for the mass of the nucleus (M) according to the equation

$$R_H = R_\infty \left(\frac{M}{M + m_e}\right)$$

S

Saturation (n.m.r.)
When the number of nuclei occupying a high energy state and a low energy state are equal, saturation is said to have taken place. This leads to a loss of the n.m.r. absorption peak, which progressively broadens and decreases in intensity as saturation is approached. This situation can be treated by the application of a powerful radio-frequency signal. The attainment of saturation is greatly dependent upon the speed with which nuclei in the higher energy state can revert to the lower energy state. In liquids this rate of relaxation (q.v.) is rapid, but in solids the excited state might persist for several minutes or even hours.

see also Longitudinal relaxation; Transverse relaxation

Saturation factor Z_0 (n.m.r.)
A mathematical factor defining the degree by which absorption signals are diminished under conditions which tend to cause equalizations of populations of nuclei in the different spin states (q.v.). For nuclei possessing a spin quantum number $I = \frac{1}{2}$

$$Z_0 = \frac{1}{1 + \gamma^2 H_1^2 T_1 T_2}$$

Scattering

When radiation is incident on a surface or passes through a transparent material a proportion of the radiation is scattered in all directions. The nature of the scattering is dependent upon the wavelength of the radiation, the nature of the substance causing the scattering and upon inhomogeneities in the material.

see also Rayleigh scattering

Schrödinger wave equation

This equation is the basis of wave mechanics and is obeyed by any moving particle.

$$\frac{\partial^2 \Psi}{\partial x^2} + \frac{\partial^2 \Psi}{\partial y^2} + \frac{\partial^2 \Psi}{\partial z^2} + \frac{8\pi^2 m}{h^2}(E - V)\Psi = 0$$

Solutions of the equation are only possible for finite, non-zero, unique values of E; such solutions are termed eigenvalues (q.v.) and correspond to the energy states developed from the Bohr theory of the atom. Ψ is termed the eigenfunction (q.v.) and $\Psi^*\Psi$ is the probability of finding the particle at a particular position defined by three coordinates x, y and z.

Scissor vibration (i.r.)

In this form of bending vibration (q.v.) the motion of the atoms leads to a change in the angle between the atoms forming the group.

Screening constant (n.m.r.)

see Nuclear screening constant; Shielding

Secondary filter (pl.)

A secondary filter is used in filter fluorimeters to absorb any reflected or scattered exciting radiation and to permit passage of only the fluorescent light. The filters (q.v.) are made from special glasses chosen to cut off radiation below a defined wavelength. A series of filters covering cut-off limits over the range 200–600 nm is available for use in fluorimeters.

Second-order (and higher-order) spin patterns (n.m.r.)

When first-order (q.v.) spin conditions no longer apply, approximately when $\Delta v < 6J$, the nature of multiplicities from spin–spin coupling (q.v.) becomes increasingly more complex. Thus the spacing and ratios of peak heights become distorted and frequently extra peaks occur. Such systems are termed second order (or occasionally a higher order than this).

Sector disc (em.)

Simplification of spectra and the determination of the coupling nuclei can be achieved by multiple-resonance techniques (q.v.) and by the use of chemical shift reagents (q.v.).

Sector disc (em.)

see Log sector; Step sector

Selection rules for atomic spectra

Certain transitions between electronic energy levels have been found to be almost totally forbidden in the formation of atomic spectra (q.v.). The selection rules enable the permitted transitions to be predicted on the basis of the differences between the quantum numbers for any two energy levels involved.

For permitted transitions

ΔL (change in orbital angular momentum) $= \pm 1$
ΔJ (change in total angular momentum) $= 0$ or ± 1
ΔM (change in magnetic orientation) $= 0$ or ± 1
ΔS (change in spin orientation) $= 0$

Shielding (n.m.r.)

Nuclear magnetic resonance absorptions occurring at high field strength do so because of the high electron density around the nuclei. They are said to be shielded and this is assisted by adjacent electropositive groups and atoms. The circulating electrons around the nuclei induce a magnetic field that is opposite to the direction of the applied magnetic field. The effective magnetic field experienced by a nucleus as a result of shielding is $H_0 - \sigma H_0$, where σH_0 is the induced field due to the electron circulation. The larger the value of σH_0, the greater is the degree of shielding and the higher the applied field necessary to bring about resonance of the nucleus (i.e. in the case of protons the nearer this will be to the TMS signal).

cf. Deshielding; Ring current effect

Shift reagents (n.m.r.)

see Chemical shift reagents

Shim coils (n.m.r.)

In the n.m.r. spectrometer it is necessary to be able to compensate for any small variation in the main magnetic field[150]. This is achieved by placing

130

conducting coils, the shim coils, at the pole faces capable of carrying an electric current that will lead to the production of additional small fields to help maintain the uniformity of the field around the sample[151]. These coils, which measure about 2·5 cm in diameter, are sometimes known as Golay coils.

They are made by designing conducting coils as patterns formed by etching thin copper sheet and placing them in sets of matching pairs, one from each set on each pole face, so that current carried by them will produce field effects around the sample. In practice a set of these shim coils may consist of up to nine different patterned pairs cemented together in two very thin sandwiches of copper sheets with insulation between.

Shpol'skii effect (pl.)
Low-temperature fluorescent spectra (< 100 K) from materials in solution frequently show improved resolution of the vibrational bands compared to spectra obtained at room temperatures; this is known as the Shpol'-skii effect[152]. The quality of the low-temperature spectra is solvent dependent, the best results being obtained when the dimensions of solvent and solute molecules are approximately equal.
see also EPA mixed solvent

Side bands (n.m.r.)
see Nuclear satellite signals; Spinning side bands

Simple cleavage (m.s.)
This is the term given to fragmentation of a single covalent bond to produce an ion and a neutral particle. Because bonds vary in strength, fragmentation of a molecule occurs at certain preferential sites and leads to relatively simple mass spectra.

Single-coil method (n.m.r.)
The bridge, or single-coil, method of measuring n.m.r. absorptions uses a radio-frequency bridge system similar to the Wheatstone bridge (q.v.) arrangement[154,155]. So that the bridge is balanced when no energy is absorbed by the sample. When absorption occurs the bridge is thrown out of balance and a signal recorded. This is achieved with just a single coil arranged around the sample tube.
cf. Induction method

131

Single-focusing mass spectrometer (m.s.)

from source → | bridge | → to detector

Figure 39. Single-coil probe

Single-focusing mass spectrometer (m.s.)

A mass spectrometer possessing only one magnetic or electric field for resolving the positive ions is termed single focusing. By far the most common of these are based upon magnetic analysers as originally developed by Dempster[156]. The resolution (q.v.) of such instruments is usually below 2000.

see also Double-focusing mass spectrometer

Figure 40. Single-focusing mass spectrometer

Singlet state (pl.)
The two electrons in any filled orbit possess equal and opposite spins which cancel each other out. This is termed a singlet state and is designated by the letter S. When radiant energy is absorbed one of the two electrons is elevated to an excited singlet state S_1 which persists for a short period of time between 10^{-4} and 10^{-8} s. From the excited state three main processes are possible; the electron may revert to the ground state by loss of energy without re-emission to the surroundings, or it may pass to a triplet state (q.v.) eventually giving rise to phosphorescence, or the third process is loss of energy and reversion to the ground state via fluorescence (q.v.).

SI units
A system of units based upon the metre, kilogramme, second, ampere, kelvin, candela and mole adopted by the Conférence Générale des Poids et Mesures in 1960. This International System of Units (Système International d'Unités) employs only one basic unit for each physical quantity[1,2,153].

Slit
In the monochromation of light in spectrometers the size of the slit and its position is of considerable importance. The amount of radiant energy entering or emerging from the monochromator is determined by the slit width which needs to be varied with the wavelength to ensure roughly constant energy from the source over the whole spectral range. This adjustment is automatically carried out in most modern spectrometers in which the slit is coupled to the rotation of the prism (q.v.) or grating (q.v.). Bilaterally symmetrical slits are now commonly used so that both sides move equally from the fixed central path of the radiation. Slit widths for infrared studies are between 10 and 1000 μm, whilst for ultraviolet work they are about 10 to 20 μm.

Smekal–Raman effect
     see Raman effect

Sodium-2, 2-dimethyl-2-silapentane-5-sulphonate (n.m.r.)
     see DSS

Solar blind detectors (u.v.)

These are special photomultipliers (q.v.) sensitive to middle- and vacuum-u.v. regions but 'blind' to solar radiation[157]. They incorporate a photo-cathode of either rubidium telluride or caesium iodide and dynodes (q.v.) of silver/magnesium[158]. The operating range is between 160 and 320 nm with a peak sensitivity at about 220 nm.

Solid deposits (i.r.)

Infrared spectra of solids may be obtained from a thin film of the solid deposited on a sodium chloride or potassium bromide plate by evaporation of a small volume of a concentrated solution of the solid. This method produces an amorphous film sufficiently thin and transparent for the infra-red radiation to pass through. The existence of large crystals leads to the production of poor spectra with broad absorption peaks.

see also Mulls; Pressed discs

Spark ionization source (m.s.)

A radio-frequency spark source employing a voltage between 6 and 60 V is one method of obtaining suitable ionization to produce mass spectra of inorganic materials[159]. The frequency of the spark is 100 Hz with a pulse duration of 100 μs. The electrodes may be prepared from a mixture of graphite and the material to be examined[160]. Quantitative analysis of impurities as low as 10 p.p.b. can be carried out by this mass spectrometric procedure.

Spectral bandwidth

see Effective bandwidth

Spectrofluorimeter (pl.)

The modern spectrofluorimeter is an automatic scanning instrument capable of studying fluorescence over a wide range of wavelengths. It consists of a radiation source (such as a xenon arc lamp), a monochromator for selection of the exciting wavelength, a sample cuvette and an emission monochromator with a photomultiplier detector. The analyser system is commonly at 90° to the source and excitation monochromator to minimize the effects of reflected and scattered radiation.

Figure 41. Optical diagram of a spectrofluorimeter

Spectrograph

This is the name given to an instrument which produces a spectrum and records it on a photographic plate. Early mass analysers were spectrographs, but the production of photographic images of spectra is now almost completely restricted to emission spectroscopy. Although it is the visible region of the spectrum that is normally examined by this means the use of special photographic plates has enabled it to be extended to the ultraviolet and near-infrared regions. Most spectrographs are prism instruments and

135

employ spark sources, they are capable of detecting less than 1 part in 10^5 of most metals.

Spectrometer (optical)
The term spectrometer is used for any instrument which produces a spectrum by dispersion (q.v.) of radiant energy and in which measurement of the transmitted energy may be made by scanning the spectrum range.

see also Mass spectrometer; Spectrophotometer

Spectrophotometer
This is a highly sophisticated spectrometer for studying emitted radiation in the infrared, visible or ultraviolet regions, incorporating devices for the automatic measurement and recording of spectra. The essential parts to such an instrument are the source, the monochromator (q.v.), the sample section, the detectors (q.v.) and the recorder. Any change of prisms or gratings during the course of scanning the spectrum is carried out automatically and the recorder provides a plot of the intensity transmitted or absorbed against the wavelength.

Spectroscopic splitting factor (e.s.r.)
see Landé factor; Nuclear *g* factor

Speed of light *c*
Measured in a vacuum this has the value of $2 \cdot 997\ 925 \times 10^8$ m s^{-1}.

Spin echo (n.m.r.)
see Pulse method

Spin–lattice relaxation T_1 (n.m.r.)
see Longitudinal relaxation

Spinning side bands (n.m.r.)
These very small peaks in the background of n.m.r. spectra are frequently observed on either side of a main absorption peak or multiplet (q.v.). They arise from inhomogeneities in the permanent magnetic field and from lack of uniformity in the spinning sample tube. The measurement in hertz between the main n.m.r. absorption and the attendant spinning side bands

is the rate of spin of the sample tube. Further spinning side bands can some-times be observed at other multiples of the spinning rate.

Spinning side bands are frequently confused with other small peaks arising in the spectrum, such as those due to nuclear satellite signals (q.v.). Their true nature can be ascertained by spinning the sample tube at different rates. The only bands that will move their positions relative to the stronger absorptions are the spinning side bands, whilst any true n.m.r. absorption signal will remain stationary.

Spin quantum number I (n.m.r.)

Most nuclei possess a nuclear spin which may occupy several orientations in the presence of a magnetic field. The spin quantum number (I) defines the number of orientations ($2I + 1$) which the nuclear magnet may occupy in the applied magnetic field. I may be of integral or half integral value, e.g. ^{1}H,$I = \frac{1}{2}$; ^{11}B,$I = \frac{3}{2}$; ^{14}N,$I = 1$. A few elements (those in which both the atomic number and the mass number are even) have $I = 0$, e.g. ^{12}C and ^{16}O.

For nuclei in which $I = \frac{1}{2}$ there are two possible orientations in the applied field: either aligned with the field; or aligned against the field. The first of these is the lower energy level.

Spin–spin coupling (n.m.r.)

This expression refers to the influence that closely situated spinning nuclei have upon each other as a result of spin effects transferred through the bonding electrons. Spin–spin coupling occurs because the bonding electron is influenced by the field produced owing to the spin of the nearest nucleus. The field of this electron will in turn affect the field of the second bonding electron which also continues the effect to the next nucleus. The overall result is that one nucleus has an indirect influence on the spin characteristics of another.

The effect diminishes with distance and rarely extends beyond four bonds between protons. Phosphorus nuclei, however, exhibit long-range spin–spin coupling that frequently extends beyond four bonds.

The result of spin–spin coupling is that any particular nucleus is influenced by the different energy states (two in the case of protons) of any nearby nucleus. As a consequence its absorption peak is split into a multiplet (q.v.).

Spin–spin decoupling (n.m.r.)

When coupling occurs with more than one proton the multiplicity of the resulting absorption can be determined from the Pascal triangle (q.v.).
see also Coupling constant; Spin–spin decoupling

Spin–spin decoupling (n.m.r.)

Spin–spin decoupling is an instrumental procedure whereby the normal spin–spin coupling (q.v.) between nuclei is prevented by irradiating the two coupled nuclei each with a radio frequency related to the difference in the chemical shifts of the two nuclei. The technique used for this is known as multiple resonance (q.v.), in its simplest form employing two radio frequencies it is double resonance.
see also INDOR; Tickling

Spin states (n.m.r.)

The number of possible orientations (spin states) that the nuclear magnet may assume under the influence of the applied magnetic field is determined by the spin quantum number (q.v.) of the nucleus. The number of nuclei occupying a particular spin state is known as the population.
see also Population inversion; Nuclear spin temperature

Spin temperature (n.m.r.)
see Nuclear spin temperature

Sputter-ion pump (m.s.)

Also called the electric discharge getter pump, this is a special device developed to produce high vacua by the ionization of any residual gases with simultaneous reaction of ions, atoms and molecules with titanium vapour[161]. After initial reduction of pressure to 10^{-2}–10^{-3} torr with a fore-pump it is possible to get down to 10^{-10} torr with the sputter-ion pump. The titanium is used in the form of a wire which is gradually unwound[162] as it is vaporized at 2000 °C.

Standard addition method (a.s.)

This approach to quantitative analysis is of wide application in spectroscopy and is particularly applicable to flame photometric determinations. The procedure involves adding a constant amount of the unknown concentration to a series of standards of the pure material and making the mixtures of unknown plus standard to equal volumes. Measurement of the spectra on the flame photometer or spectrometer at a selected wavelength, using each solution individually, produces a series of values which can be plotted against the concentration of the standards. Extrapolation of the line through these points gives an intersection on the concentration line corresponding to the negative value of the unknown concentration. This can also be calculated from the slope of the line without resorting to extrapolation[163].

The method is used when other substances are present that are likely to introduce errors and interferences. Its value is limited to linear emission/concentration ranges.

Stark–Einstein law
Each molecule taking part in a photochemical reaction absorbs one quantum of the radiation leading to the reaction taking place.

see Einstein

Stefan–Boltzmann constant σ
The value of this constant applicable in the Stefan–Boltzmann law (q.v.) is given by

$$\sigma = \frac{2\pi^5 k^4}{15h^3 c^2} = 5\cdot669\ 61 \times 10^{-8} \text{ W m}^{-2} \text{ K}^{-4}$$

Stefan–Boltzmann law
The total radiation M from unit area of a black body (q.v.) in unit time is proportional to the fourth power of the absolute temperature of the body.

$$M = \sigma T^4$$

This relationship is obtained by integrating the equation from the Planck law of radiation (q.v.).

see also Wien laws; Rayleigh and Jeans law

Step sector (em.)
Rotation of a step sector placed in the light path of an emission spectrograph produces spectral lines of graduated intensity along the length of each line. This is because the sector reduces the effective light intensity reaching the photographic plate to a fraction equal to the ratio of the area of the cut-away sectors. The device is used to determine the exposure/line density characteristics for the photographic emulsion[102], figure 42.

cf. Log sector

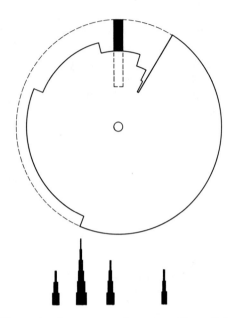

Figure 42. Step sector (appearance of spectrum lines of different intensity indicated below)

Stigmatic

In the spectroscopic sense this means that light from both horizontal and vertical lines is focused at the same distance so that astigmatic (q.v.) distortions do not occur. It is used with reference to diffraction gratings (q.v.) and the associated optical systems.

Stokes law (pl.)

This law states that the wavelength of a fluorescent emission is always longer than that of the exciting wavelength. This is why substances which appear colourless when viewed in visible light frequently appear coloured when fluorescing under ultraviolet light.

Stokes lines (r.s.)

The Raman lines occurring on the longer-wavelength side of the mono-chromatic radiation source line are termed Stokes lines. They arise from those Raman transitions in which the final vibrational level is higher than

140

the initial vibrational level. These are normally measured in preference to the anti-Stokes lines (q.v.) as they are stronger.

see also Raman spectroscopy

Stretching vibrations (i.r.)

A molecule composed of n atoms exhibits $3n - 6$ vibrational modes, or $3n - 5$ if it is linear. Of these $n - 1$ modes are valence (or stretching) vibrations. That is, the movement occurs along the bonds between the atoms concerned. The two possible stretching vibrations for a triatomic molecule are shown in the figure below.

cf. Bending vibrations

Figure 43. Stretching vibrations

Sweep coils (n.m.r.)

Scanning of the spectrum in n.m.r. spectroscopy is usually carried out by varying the magnetic field in which the sample is situated, rather than by varying the radio-frequency field. The sweep over the spectrum range is achieved by passing a current through coils either wound round the pole pieces or situated between the pole faces and the sample. In the second case these constitute a Helmholtz pair in which the distance between the coils is equal to the radius of the coils, as this produces a good uniform field.

N.B. These are not the shim coils (q.v.).

Symmetry (i.r.)

see Axis of symmetry; Centre of symmetry; Plane of symmetry

T

Tantalum boat (a.s.)

This is a microsampling technique developed for atomic absorption spectroscopy in which the sample is placed in a small tantalum dish and inserted into the flame of the spectrometer. This procedure is similar to the Delves cup (q.v.) method that was developed particularly for the study of blood samples.

Tau values τ **(n.m.r.)**

               see Parts per million

Tesla T

               see Magnetic flux density

Tetramethylsilane (n.m.r.)

               see TMS

Thermal emission ion source (m.s.)
The evaporation of a substance from a heated surface leads to the formation of positive ions, and this process has been developed as a method for the production of ions for mass spectrometry. The method is used particularly to study isotopic abundance of heavier elements. Operating temperatures as high as 3000 °C are employed and the substance is heated on tungsten or tantalum supports[164]. Useful spectra have been obtained with less than 15 μg of material.

Thermistor (i.r.)
The word thermistor is a contraction for 'thermal resistor'—substances which change their resistance with temperature. Those developed as infrared detectors are usually known as bolometers (q.v.).

Thermocouple (i.r.)
In the thermocouple detector the infrared radiation falls onto a metal junction formed from two dissimilar metals. The change in temperature of the junction causes a current to flow through the metals and this is amplified and fed to a recorder. For the purposes of infrared detection in spectrometers the thermocouple junction is usually welded to a small strip (2 × 0·2 mm²) of blackened gold leaf[165]. The thermocouple may also be combined with a large number of identical junctions to form a thermopile (q.v.).

Thermopile (i.r.)
A thermopile is formed from a number of thermocouples (q.v.) joined to produce a series of alternate hot and cold junctions arranged in rows close to each other[166]. The radiation falls on the blackened metal foil forming the

heat-sensitive junctions and the temperature difference between this and the combined cold junctions leads to the current flow associated with any thermocouple system. A complete thermopile for use as an infrared detector may have up to twenty hot junctions made from silver and bismuth wires, the foil radiation receiver being blackened gold or platinum.

Tickling (n.m.r.)
Tickling is one of the modified forms of the double-resonance technique in which the extent of spin–spin coupling (q.v.) is reduced by bringing about partial perturbation of one of the coupled nuclei. In this process one transition is selectively irradiated, but only to the extent that a complete collapse of the resonance peak does not occur. This tickling procedure enables the coupled nuclei to be identified from the small change in the spectrum without recourse to the full multiple-resonance (q.v.) technique.

Time constant (i.r.)
This is sometimes used as a measure of the slowness of reponse of a detector in a spectophotometer. It is normally understood to mean the time needed for the detector to show a drop of 63 % when the irradiation is discontinued.
cf. Response time

Time-of-flight mass spectrometer (m.s.)
In this instrument ions of different mass/charge ratios are separated according to the time taken to travel along a fixed horizontal path, known as the drift tube (q.v.)[167]. The ions arrive at the end of the tube in increasing order of their mass/charge ratios. To avoid overlapping spectra the ion source operates in a series of pulses and produces a complete mass spectrum every 100 μs, although the detector is only scanning a small part of the spectrum at any particular period of time[168], figure 44.

Separation of ions is governed by the equation

$$\frac{m}{e} = \frac{2Vt^2}{l^2}$$

from which it can be shown that for the ions

$$\text{velocity} \propto \frac{1}{\sqrt{m}}$$

see also Continuous mode; Pulsed mode

143

Figure 44. Schematic diagram of time-of-flight mass spectrometer

TMS (n.m.r.)

Tetramethylsilane $(CH_3)_4Si$ is now the accepted standard as the reference signal for proton n.m.r. spectra[169]. All the twelve protons absorb at the same magnetic field strength which is at higher field strength than for the protons in almost every other substance. All chemical shifts (q.v.) are then referred to the TMS peak which is specified as absorbing at 0 Hz $(0 \text{ p.p.m.} \delta \equiv 10 \text{ p.p.m.} \tau)$.

It is a chemically inert liquid boiling at 27 °C. This low boiling point presents difficulties when n.m.r. spectra are determined at elevated temperatures and a secondary standard such as chloroform may be used in place of TMS. As it is also insoluble in heavy water (D_2O) it is necessary to use the water soluble standard DSS (q.v.) in this case.

Toronto arc (r.s.)

Before the advent of the laser (q.v.) the Toronto mercury arc source was for many years the standard device for producing monochromatic visible light for Raman spectroscopy (q.v.). Both the 4358 Å and 5461 Å lines were selected for these studies. It has now been almost completely displaced because of the stronger sources available from gas lasers.

144

One of the disadvantages in using arc sources was that filters of aqueous solutions of sodium nitrite or potassium chromate had to be used to prevent interferences due to fluorescence and shorter-wavelength radiations, and as heat filters.

Figure 45. Toronto type mercury arc lamp

Torr (m.s.)

see Pressure, units

Transmittance *T* (i.r., u.v.)
This is the ratio of the radiant energy transmitted by a substance to the radiant energy incident upon that substance.

$$T = \frac{I}{I_0}$$

Values obtained for transmittance are usually given as percentages.

145

The words transmittancy and transmission have been used for this ratio, but transmittance has met with general acceptance and is now recommended[1].

see also Absorbance; Molar extinction coefficient

Transverse relaxation T_2 (n.m.r.)

One of the two methods by which nuclear spin energy may be lost from one nucleus is by the transfer to another nucleus of the same isotope. This is transverse relaxation and leads to broadening of an n.m.r. absorption peak. It does not result in any change in the numbers of nuclei occupying the different energy levels. The linewidth is inversely proportional to T_2 and is related to the degree of uncertainty in the energy states. The results of transverse relaxation are commonly seen in the n.m.r. spectra of viscous liquids and of solids.

Triplet state (e.s.r., pl.)

The triplet state can only arise from the promotion of one of the two π electrons, forming part of an unsaturated system, to an upper unoccupied orbital. If the spin of the promoted electron is the same as that of the unexcited electron, they are said to be parallel and the spin quantum number (S) is $\frac{1}{2} + \frac{1}{2} = 1$. This leads to a multiplicity of possible states given by $2S + 1 = 3$ in which the three values correspond to three slightly different energy levels so that the electrons are said to be in a triplet state.

The triplet state is a lower energy state than is the corresponding singlet state (q.v.) and is sometimes referred to as a metastable state. Electrons can remain in the triplet state for extended periods of time, several seconds, and may revert to the ground state by emission of radiation as phosphorescence (q.v.).

Tungsten filament lamp (i.r., u.v.)

Although the tungsten filament lamp is usually employed as the source of radiant energy for the visible region (400–800 nm) of the spectrum it may also be used as a source for the near-infrared region as its effective operating range extends as high as 3 μm.

The lamp consists of an incandescent tungsten filament in a glass enclosure. The operating temperature is about 2300 °C and requires a voltage fluctuation of less than 0·01 V to give a constant radiation output.

Incorporation of a small amount of iodine in the tungsten lamp envelope enables operation at higher temperature and an extension of the useful range to below 400 nm.

Twisting vibration (i.r.)
A bending vibration (q.v.) in which atoms of the same group move in the same plane but in opposite directions to each other.

cf. Stretching vibrations

U

Ultraviolet/visible spectrum
The ultraviolet region of the electromagnetic spectrum (q.v.) is usually considered as that section between 10 and 380 nm, whilst the visible region is between 380 and 780 nm. Spectrophotometers (q.v.) are manufactured to study both the near-ultraviolet and the visible regions with a continuous scan from 200 to 780 nm. The region with wavelengths shorter than 210 nm is known as the vacuum-ultraviolet region and requires specially modified instruments for study to be made[170].

see also Gratings; Prisms; Spectrophotometers

Figure 46. Ultraviolet/visible spectrum of potassium permanganate

147

u mode (n.m.r.)

The absorption signal plotted for the nuclear magnetic resonance spectrum is accompanied by another signal called the 'dispersion' or 'u mode' signal. This is out of phase with the absorption and is eliminated by the detector phase control. The theoretical Lorentzian line shape (q.v.) of the dispersion curve can be calculated from the Bloch equations (q.v.).

V

Valence vibrations (i.r.)

see Stretching vibrations

Variable path-length cell (i.r.)

see Liquid cell

Velocity of light c

This is identical for all wavelengths and is usually given as the velocity of light in a vacuum with the value

$$c = 2.997\,925\,0 \times 10^8 \text{ m s}^{-1} \approx 3 \times 10^{10} \text{ cm s}^{-1}$$

Vibrational spectra (i.r., r.s.)

Vibrational spectra are observed when the absorption of radiant energy causes a change in the energy of a molecular vibration. These transitions are accompanied by changes in the rotational state of the molecule and are observed in the region 4000–400 cm^{-1} (2.5–25 μm) as infrared (q.v.) and Raman spectra (q.v.).

Virtual coupling (n.m.r.)

If a nucleus is coupled to another nucleus that in turn is coupled to a third nucleus possessing a similar chemical shift (q.v.) as the second nucleus, a long-range coupling effect between the first and third nuclei occurs. As a result the simple multiplet (q.v.) pattern for the absorption of the first proton is complicated by further splitting which produces a distorted, non-uniform appearance to the observed absorption spectrum. Virtual coupling of this type is common in molecules possessing long alkyl chains.

Visible spectrum
    see Electromagnetic spectrum; Ultraviolet/visible spectrum

v mode (n.m.r.)
This is the normal absorption signal measured and recorded in n.m.r. spectroscopy. It is out of phase with the dispersion, u-mode (q.v.), signal.

W

Wadsworth mounting (em.)
Of the different forms of mounting employed for emission spectrographs the Wadsworth has been particularly successful as it is stigmatic (q.v.)

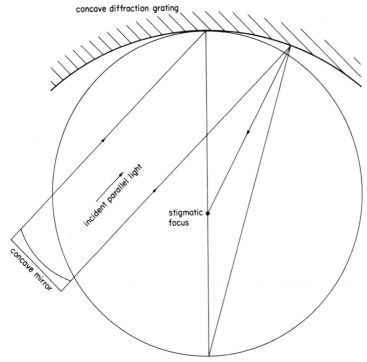

Figure 47. Wadsworth mounting

whilst most other emission mountings are astigmatic (q.v.). It achieves this by employing a concave diffraction grating in place of the conventional plane surface grating (q.v.). The arrangement is illustrated in figure 47.

Wagging vibration (i.r.)
Of the four types of bending vibrations (q.v.) the wagging vibration is one in which there is no change in the angle between the bonds of the vibrating group. This is because the vibration takes place in a plane at right angles to the plane of the group.

Watson–Biemann separator (m.s.)
This particular type of interface (q.v.) between a gas chromatograph and a mass spectrometer consists of a long (20 cm), narrow (8 mm) porous glass diffusion tube. Effluent gases from the gas chromatograph pass along the tube and the helium carrier gas diffuses through the pores more rapidly than do the heavier organic molecules[171]. As a result a fifty-fold enrichment of the sample is obtained.

Wave equation
see Schrödinger wave equation

Waveguides (e.s.r.)
These are rectangular (or sometimes circular) cross section metal tubes used to direct the microwaves generated by the klystron (q.v.) oscillator used in an e.s.r. spectrometer. They are made from brass plated with silver.

The waves pass along the waveguides by reflection from the walls of the tube. Waveguides are employed because at microwave frequencies transmission losses are substantial if conventional means are used. The dimensions of the waveguides influence the field patterns created by the microwaves and it is normal to employ a waveguide with a cross-section dimension comparable with the frequency being generated by the klystron, e.g. approximately 2 cm × 1 cm.

Wavelength λ
The linear distance measured along the line of propagation of the wave between any two points that are in phase on adjacent waves. For the sake of

convenience the measurement is normally taken between maxima or minima on the wave diagram.

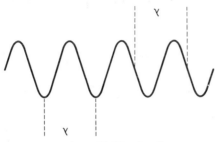

Figure 48. Wavelength

Wavenumber $\tilde{\nu}$ or σ (i.r.)
In addition to the above two symbols used for this function the symbol k is employed in solid-state physics.

It is related to wavelength (q.v.) and frequency (q.v.) by the following equation:

$$\tilde{\nu}(\sigma) = \frac{\nu}{c} = \frac{1}{\lambda}$$

and is usually expressed in reciprocal centimetres (cm^{-1}).

Weber Wb
The SI unit (q.v.) of magnetic flux (Φ) is the weber, related to other units as follows:

$$\text{Wb} = \text{m}^2\,\text{kg}\,\text{s}^2\,\text{A}^{-1} = \text{V}\,\text{s}$$

and $1\,\text{Wb} = 10^8$ maxwell.

Wedge

see Attenuator

Wheatstone bridge circuit
In the circuit shown below if the four resistances satisfy the equation $R_1/R_2 = R_3/R_4$ then no current flows through the galvanometer. This type of circuit is the basis of potentiometry and is used in spectrophotometers

151

(q.v.) incorporating resistance type detectors such as the bolometer (q.v.). The change in resistance of the detector throws the bridge circuit out of balance and the resulting signal can be fed to a recorder.

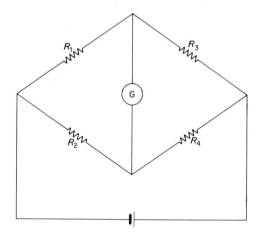

Figure 49. Wheatstone bridge circuit

Wien laws

These three laws on black-body radiation (q.v.) pre-date the Planck law of radiation (q.v.) but can be derived from it. They are as follows.

(a) The wavelength of the maximum of the intensity of radiation from the black-body source is inversely proportional to the absolute temperature.

$$\lambda_{max}T = \text{constant}$$

(b) The radiant exitance at the wavelength maximum is proportional to the fifth power of the absolute temperature.

$$M_{\lambda_{max}}T^{-5} = \text{constant}$$

(c) The spectral radiant exitance is given by

$$M_\lambda = \frac{2\pi hc^2\lambda^{-5}}{e^{hc/kT\lambda} - 1}$$

see also Stefan–Boltzmann law; Rayleigh and Jeans law

Wiggle-beat method (n.m.r.)

Rapid scanning of two closely spaced absorption signals leads to super-imposition of the ringing (q.v.) of the two signals to form a beat pattern. The frequency of the beat is equal to the separation of the signals and arises from the inability of the nuclear magnetization to keep pace with the applied field.

Woodward rules (u.v.)

Structural modifications to a chromophoric system (q.v.) frequently show a simple additive relationship. By assigning a value (in nm) to each functional part of a molecule and adding them together it is possible to predict where the major absorption for the system will arise[172]. Woodward[173] applied this procedure extensively to his study of sterols and related compounds.

Wratten filter

Used in simple colorimeters, this filter consists of a thin film of dyed gelatine sandwiched between two pieces of glass. The filter deteriorates with time due to decomposition of the dyes.

X

Xenon arc lamp (a.s., u.v.)

This radiation source is employed in u.v./visible and in fluorescent spectroscopy when a very high level of continuous illumination is required. A 150 W xenon arc source operating on d.c. is most commonly used, the useful radiation range being between 220 and 850 nm. It has been used to obtain rapid analyses by atomic fluorescence[174] with detection limits below 5 p.p.m. for many elements[175].

X, Y and Z gradients (n.m.r.) .

The three mutually perpendicular axes are used to relate the parts of the probe (q.v.) in the n.m.r. spectrometer to the magnet system. The X axis is taken as that perpendicular to the sample tube and parallel to the magnet faces (pole pieces); the Y axis is along the length of the sample tube; the Z axis is through the centres of the pole pieces and perpendicular to the sample tube.

Z

Zeeman effect

This is the effect of overcoming the normal degeneracy of electron spin states by applying a magnetic field which can interact with the magnetic moment of the electron. The Zeeman effect is observed when atoms are subjected to a powerful magnetic field resulting in the spectral lines being split into a number of component lines.

The energy level difference is given by

$$\Delta E = m_i g \mu_B H$$

The energy levels are sometimes referred to as Zeeman levels and in effect it is transitions between these levels that are measured in electron spin resonance spectroscopy (q.v.).

References

1. 'Quantities, units and symbols', *A Report by the Symbols Committee of the Royal Society*, London (1971).
2. *Manual of Symbols and Terminology for Physicochemical Quantities and Units*, International Union of Pure and Applied Chemistry, Butterworths, London (1970). Also published in *Pure Appl. Chem.*, **21**, No. 1 (1970).
3. C. Moser and A. I. Kohlenberg, *J. Chem. Soc.*, 804 (1951).
4. 'Spectrometry nomenclature', *Anal. Chem.*, **37**, 1814 (1965).
5. J. H. Beynon and A. E. Williams, *Mass and Abundance Tables for Use in Mass Spectrometry*, Elsevier, London (1963).
6. C. A. Parker, *Proc. Soc. Anal. Chem. Conf.*, *Nottingham* (Ed. P. W. Shallis), W. Heffer and Sons Ltd., London (1955).
7. H. C. Kahn, *J. Chem. Educ.*, **43**, A7, A103 (1966).
8. T. S. West, *Chem. Ind.*, 387 (1970).
9. J. J. Balmer, *Ann. Physik*, **25**, 80 (1885).
10. J. Fahrenfort, *Spectrochim. Acta*, **17**, 698 (1961).
11. N. J. Harrick, *Internal Reflection Spectroscopy*, Interscience, New York (1967).
12. S. Nagakura and J. Tanaka, *J. Chem. Phys.*, **22**, 236 (1954).
13. W. F. Forbes and R. Shilton, in *Symp. Spectrosc.*, *ASTM Spec. Tech. Publ.*, No. 269, 176 (1960).
14. A. Burawoy, *J. Chem. Soc.*, 1177 (1939).
15. K. Bowden and E. A. Braude, *J. Chem. Soc.*, 1068 (1952).
16. L. Doub and J. H. Vandenbelt, *J. Am. Chem. Soc.*, **69**, 2714 (1947).
17. H. B. Klevens and J. R. Platt, *J. Am. Chem. Soc.*, **71**, 1714 (1949).
18. E. Clar, *Aromatische Kohlenwasserstoffe*, Springer–Verlag, Berlin (1952).
19. N. Wright, *Anal. Chem.*, **13**, 1 (1941).
20. G. Pirlot, *Bull. Soc. Chim. Belg.*, **58**, 28, 48 (1949).
21. J. H. Lambert, *Photometria sive de Mensura et Gradibus Luminis, Colorum et Umbrae*, Angsburg (1760); reprinted in Otswald, *Klassiker der Exakten Wissenschaften*, No. 32, 64 (1892).
22. M. Bouguer, *Essai d'Optique sur la Gradation de la Lumiere*, Paris

References

(1729); see also Otswald, *Klassiker der Exakten Wissenschaften,* No. 33, 58 (1892). M. Bouguer, *Traité d'Optique sur la Gradation de la Lumiere, Ouvrage Posthume,* Pub. de Lacaille (1760).

23. A. Beer, *Ann. Physik Chem.* (J. C. Poggendorff), **86,** 78 (1852).
24. F. Bernard, *Ann. Chim. Phys.,* **35,** [3], 385 (1852).
25. D. R. Malinin and J. H. Yoe, *J. Chem. Educ.,* **38,** 129 (1961).
26. F. H. Lohman, *J. Chem. Educ.,* **32,** 155 (1955).
27. F. Bloch, *Phys. Rev.,* **70,** 460 (1946).
28. F. Bloch, *Phys. Rev.,* **102,** 104 (1956).
29. R. M. Milton, *Chem. Rev.,* **39,** 419 (1946).
30. W. H. Brattain and J. A. Becker, *J. Opt. Soc. Am.,* **36,** 354 (1946).
31. N. Fuson, *J. Opt. Soc. Am.,* **38,** 845 (1948).
32. B. D. Flockhart and R. C. Pink, *Talanta,* **12,** 546 (1965).
33. *Tables of Wavenumbers for the Calibration of Infrared Spectrometers,* I.U.P.A.C., Butterworths, London (1961).
34. *Pure Appl. Chem.,* **1,** [4], 537–699 (1961).
35. R. G. Anderson, I. S. Maines and T. W. West, *Anal. Chim. Acta,* **51,** 335 (1970).
36. J. F. Alder and T. S. West, *Anal. Chim. Acta.,* **51,** 365 (1970).
37. C. A. Parker, *Proc. Roy. Soc. (London), Ser. A,* **220,** 104 (1953).
38. J. N. Pitts, G. W. Cowell and D. R. Burley, *Environmental Sci. Tech.,* **2,** 435 (1968).
39. R. M. Silverstein and G. C. Bassler, *Spectrometric Identification of Organic Compounds,* 2nd edn., Wiley, New York, p. 116 (1967).
40. C. C. Hinckley, *J. Am. Chem. Soc.,* **91,** 5160 (1969).
41. W. D. Horrocks and J. P. Sipe, *J. Am. Chem. Soc.,* **93,** 6800 (1971).
42. J. Briggs, F. A. Hart, G. P. Moss and E. W. Randall, *Chem. Commun.,* 364 (1971).
43. M. Czerny and A. F. Turner, *Z. Physik,* **61,** 792 (1930).
44. W. G. Fastie, *J. Opt. Soc. Am.,* **42,** 641 (1952).
45. H. Ebert, *Wied Ann.,* 489 (1889).
46. H. T. Delves, *Analyst,* **95,** 431 (1970).
47. K. Morita, H. Sunahara, T. Ishizuka, N. Nakayama and S. Yamada, *J. Spectrosc. Soc. Japan,* **16,** 169 (1968); *Chem. Abstracts,* **69,** 56728 (1968).
48. B. Findeisen and W. Schuffenhauer, *Neue Huette,* **15,** 437 (1970); *Chem. Abstracts,* **73,** 116009 (1970).

49. R. M. Dagnall, K. C. Thompson and T. S. West, *Talanta*, **14,** 551 (1967).
50. K. M. Aldous, D. Alder, R. M. Dagnall and T. S. West, *Lab. Pract.*, **19,** 589 (1970).
51. G. W. Ewing, *J. Chem. Educ.*, **46,** 2, A69 (1969).
52. J. E. Wertz and J. R. Bolton, *Electron Spin Resonance, Elementary Theory and Applications*, McGraw-Hill, New York (1972).
53. G. Feher, *Phys. Rev.*, **103,** 834 (1956).
54. B. Stevens and E. Hutton, *Spectrochim. Acta*, **18,** 425 (1962).
55. B. Stevens, M. S. Walker and E. Hutton, *Proc. Chem. Soc.*, 62 (1963).
56. A. C. Hardy and F. H. Perrin, *The Principles of Optics*, McGraw-Hill, New York, p. 556 (1932).
57. Féry, *J. Phys.*, **9,** 762 (1910); *Astrophys. J.*, **34,** 79 (1911).
58. H. Budzikiewicz, C. Djerassi and D. H. Williams, *Interpretation of Mass Spectra of Organic Compounds*, Holden–Day, San Francisco (1964).
59. H. H. Willard, L. L. Merritt and J. A. Dean, *Instrumental Methods of Analysis*, 4th edn., Van Nostrand Reinhold, New York, Chap. 11, p. 309 (1965).
60. E. E. Pickett and S. R. Koirtyohann, *Anal. Chem.*, **41,** [14], 28A (1969).
61. E. Mavrodineanu, *Spectrochim. Acta*, **17,** 1016 (1961).
62. L. R. P. Butler and A. Fulton, *Appl. Opt.*, **7,** 2131 (1968).
63. B. L. Van Duuren and T. L. Chan, *Advan. Anal. Chem. Instrum.*, **9,** 387 (1971).
64. W. H. Melhuish, *J. Opt. Soc. Am.*, **52,** 1256 (1962).
65. C. A. Parker, *Photoluminescence of Solutions*, Elsevier, London, p. 128 (1969).
66. W. Gordy, *J. Chem. Phys.*, **14,** 305 (1946).
67. R. R. Ernst and W. A. Anderson, *Rev. Sci. Instrum.*, **37,** 93 (1966).
68. P. L. Richards, *J. Opt. Soc. Am.*, **54,** 1474 (1964).
69. W. J. Hurley, *J. Chem. Educ.*, **43,** 236 (1966).
70. J. Franck, *Trans. Faraday Soc.*, **21,** 536 (1926).
71. A. G. Gaydon and H. G. Wolfhard, *Flames, Their Structure, Radiation and Temperature*, Chapman and Hall, London (1953).
72. M. J. O'Neal and T. P. Wier, *Anal. Chem.*, **23,** 830 (1951).
73. S. Silvermann, *J. Opt. Soc. Am.*, **38,** 989 (1948).
74. J. V. Sullivan and A. Walsh, *Spectrochim. Acta*, **21,** 721 (1965).

References

75. J. S. Cartwright, C. Sebens and W. Slavin, *Atomic Absorption Newsletter*, **5**, 22 (1966).
76. W. J. Price, *Analytical Atomic Absorption Spectrometry*, Heyden, London, p. 37 (1972).
77. A. Paschen, *Physik*, **50**, 901 (1916).
78. W. G. Jones and A. Walsh, *Spectrochim. Acta*, **11**, 249 (1960).
79. A. D. Cross and R. A. Jones, *An Introduction to Practical Infra-red Spectroscopy*, 3rd edn., Butterworths, London, p. 43 (1969).
80. E. B. Baker, *J. Chem. Phys.*, **37**, 911 (1962); **45**, 609 (1966).
81. F. A. L. Anet and J. L. Sudmeier, *J. Magnetic Resonances*, **1**, 124 (1969).
82. F. Bloch, W. W. Hansen and M. Packard, *Phys. Rev.*, **70**, 474 (1946).
83. H. Levinstein, *Anal. Chem.*, **41**, 14, 81A (1969).
84. K. D. Möller and W. G. Rothschild, *Far-infrared Spectroscopy*, Wiley, New York (1971).
85. D. I. Rees, *Talanta*, **16**, 903 (1969).
86. S. E. Wiberley, J. W. Sprague and J. E. Campbell, *Anal. Chem.*, **29**, 210 (1957).
87. R. B. Barnes, R. C. Gore, E. F. Williams, S. G. Linsley and E. M. Peterson, *Anal. Chem.*, **19**, 620 (1947).
88. J. H. Beynon, *Mass Spectrometry and its Applications to Organic Chemistry*, Elsevier, London, p. 459 (1960).
89. M. Karplus, *J. Chem. Phys.*, **30**, 11 (1959).
90. M. Karplus, *J. Am. Chem. Soc.*, **85**, 2870 (1963).
91. *Trans. of the Joint Committee for Spectroscopy, J. Opt. Soc. Am.*, **43**, 410 (1953).
92. *Trans. of the Joint Committee for Spectroscopy, J. Opt. Soc. Am.*, **46**, 145 (1956).
93. W. A. Chupka and M. G. Inghram, *J. Phys. Chem.*, **59**, 100 (1955).
94. W. B. Rodney and I. H. Malitson, *J. Opt. Soc. Am.*, **46**, 956 (1956).
95. T. R. Gilson and P. J. Hendra, *Laser Raman Spectroscopy*, Wiley–Interscience, London (1970).
96. I. R. Beattie, *Chem. Brit.*, **6**, 347 (1967).
97. V. V. Panteleev and A. A. Yankovskii, *J. Appl. Spectrosc. (Zh. Prikli. Spectrosk.)*, **3**, 260 (1965).
98. D. C. Damoth, *Modern Aspects of Mass Spectrometry* (Ed. R. I. Reed), Plenum Press, New York, p. 49 (1968).

99. F. J. Vastola and A. J. Pirone, *Advan. Mass Spectrometry*, **4**, 107 (1968).

100. S. P. S. Porto and D. L. Wood, *J. Opt. Soc. Am.*, **52**, 251 (1962).

101. J. S. Griffith and L. E. Orgel, *Quart. Rev.*, **11**, 381 (1957).

102. *Analytical Emission Spectroscopy*, Vol. 1 (Ed. E. L. Grove), Dekker, New York, Part 1, p. 32 (1971).

103. J. A. Gilpin and F. W. McLafferty, *Anal. Chem.*, **29**, 990 (1957).

104. J. J. Thomson, *Phil. Mag.*, **21**, 225 (1911).

105. F. W. Aston, *Phil. Mag.*, **38**, 707 (1919).

106. H. Massmann, *Spectrochim. Acta*, **23B**, 215 (1968).

107. J. R. Partington, *An Advanced Treatise on Physical Chemistry*, Vol. 1, Longmans, London, p. 303 (1949).

108. J. H. Beynon, *Advan. Mass Spectrometry*, **4**, 123 (1968).

109. J. H. Beynon, R. A. Saunders and A. E. Williams, *Table of Metastable Transitions for Use in Mass Spectrometry*, Elsevier, London (1965).

110. R. N. Jones and A. Nadeau, *Spectrochim. Acta*, **12**, 183 (1958).

111. D. S. Erley, 'Long-path infrared microcell', in *Spectroscopic Tricks* (Ed. L. May), A. Hilger Ltd., London, p. 185 (1968).

112. D. R. Lide, in *Advan. Anal. Chem. Instrum.* (Eds. C. N. Reilley and F. W. McLafferty), **5**, 235 (1966).

113. R. L. Mössbauer, *Z. Physik*, **151**, 124 (1958).

114. L. May, *Appl. Spectrosc.*, **23**, 204 (1969).

115. V. I. Goldanskii and R. H. Herber, *Chemical Applications of Mössbauer Spectroscopy*, Academic Press, New York (1968).

116. R. H. Herber, *Sci. Am.*, **225**, 86 (1971).

117. J. D. Baldeschwieler and E. W. Randall, *Chem. Rev.*, **63**, 81 (1963).

118. W. McFarlane, *Chem. Brit.*, **5**, 142 (1969).

119. J. Stupar and J. B. Dawson, *Appl. Opt.*, **7**, 1351 (1968).

120. G. Uny and J. Spitz, *Spectrochim. Acta*, **25B**, 391 (1970); *Chem. Abstracts*, **73**, 132441 (1970).

121. C. W. Munday, *J. Sci. Instrum.*, **25**, 418 (1948).

122. R. M. Lynden-Bell and R. K. Harris, *Nuclear Magnetic Resonance Spectroscopy*, Nelsons, London (1969).

123. M. Kubo and D. Nakamura, *Advan. Inorg. Radiochem.*, **8**, 257 (1966).

124. C. T. O'Konski, 'Nuclear quadrupole resonance spectroscopy', in *Determination of Organic Structures by Physical Methods* (Eds. F. C.

Nachod and W. D. Phillips), Vol. 2, Academic Press, New York, Chap. 11 (1962).

125. G. C. Lyle and R. E. Lyle, 'Optical rotary dispersion', in *Determination of Organic Structures by Physical Methods* (Eds. F. C. Nachod and W. D. Phillips), Vol. 2, Academic Press, New York, Chap. 1 (1962).

126. R. A. Dwek, R. E. Richards and D. Taylor, *Ann. Rept. Nucl. Magnetic Resonance Spectrosc.*, **2**, 293 (1969).

127. K. H. Hauser and D. Stehlik, *Advan. Magnetic Resonances*, **3**, 79 (1968).

128. J. R. Dyer, *Applications of Absorption Spectroscopy of Organic Compounds*, Prentice–Hall, Englewood Cliffs, N.J., p. 52 (1965).

129. D. S. Parasnis, *Magnetism*, Hutchinson, London, p. 50 (1961).

130. G. M. Barrow, *Physical Chemistry*, McGraw-Hill, New York, p. 307 (1961).

131. R. A. Smith, *Advan. Phys.*, **2**, 321 (1953).

132. J. B. Pearce, K. A. Gause, E. F. Mackey, K. K. Kelly, W. G. Fastie and C. A. Barth, *Appl. Opt.*, **10**, 805 (1971).

133. R. Mavrodineanu and R. C. Hughes, *Spectrochim. Acta*, **19**, 1309 (1963).

134. C. D. West and D. N. Hume, *Anal. Chem.*, **36**, 412 (1964).

135. M. J. E. Golay, *Rev. Sci. Instrum.*, **18**, 347, 357 (1947).

136. M. J. E. Golay, *Rev. Sci. Instrum.*, **20**, 816 (1949).

137. G. K. T. Conn and G. K. Eaton, *J. Opt. Soc. Am.*, **44**, 553 (1954).

138. R. Newman and R. S. Halford, *Rev. Sci. Instrum.*, **19**, 270 (1948).

139. G. R. Bird and M. Parrish, *J. Opt. Soc. Am.*, **50**, 886 (1960).

140. *Perkin Elmer Instrum. News*, **16**, [3], 5 (1966).

141. J. B. Young, H. H. Graham and E. W. Peterson, *Appl. Opt.*, **4**, 1023 (1965).

142. J. G. Calvert and J. N. Pitts, *Photochemistry*, Wiley, New York, p. 728 (1966).

143. A. R. Fairbairn, *Rev. Sci. Instrum.*, **40**, 380 (1969).

144. G. Lawson and J. F. J. Todd, *Chem. Brit.*, **8**, 373 (1972).

145. A. Smekal, *Naturwissenschaften*, **11**, 873 (1923).

146. C. V. Raman and K. S. Krishnan, *Nature*, **121**, 501, 619 (1928).

147. B. P. Stoicheff, *Experimental Physics: Molecular Physics*, Vol. 3 (Ed. D. Williams), Academic Press, New York, p. 111 (1962).

148. H. E. Hallam, *Roy. Inst. Chem. Rev.*, **1**, 39 (1968).

149. A. D. Buckingham, *Can. J. Chem.*, **38,** 300 (1960).

150. M. J. E. Golay, *Rev. Sci. Instrum.*, **29,** 313 (1958).

151. W. A. Anderson, *Rev. Sci. Instrum.*, **32,** 241 (1961).

152. E. V. Shpol'skii, *Soviet Phys.—Usp.* (*Engl. Transl.*), **3,** 372 (1960).

153. N. H. Davies, *Chem. Brit.*, **6,** 344 (1970); **7,** 331 (1971).

154. E. M. Purcell, H. C. Torrey and R. V. Pound, *Phys. Rev.*, **69,** 37 (1946).

155. N. E. M. Bloembergen, E. M. Purcell and R. V. Pound, *Phys. Rev.*, **73,** 679 (1948).

156. A. J. Dempster, *Phys. Rev.*, **11,** 316 (1918).

157. R. W. Engstrom, *J. Opt. Soc. Am.*, **37,** 420 (1947).

158. L. Dunkelman, W. B. Fowler and J. Hennes, *Appl. Opt.*, **1,** 695 (1962).

159. A. Cornu, *Advan. Mass. Spectrometry*, **4,** 401 (1968).

160. C. A. Evans and G. H. Morrison, *Anal. Chem.*, **40,** 869, 2106 (1968).

161. R. H. Davis and A. S. Divatia, *Rev. Sci. Instrum.*, **25,** 1193 (1954).

162. R. G. Herb, R. H. Davis, A. S. Divatia and D. Saxon, *Phys. Rev.*, **89,** 897 (1953).

163. H. H. Willard, L. L. Merritt and J. A. Dean, *Instrumental Methods of Analysis*, 4th edn., Van Nostrand Reinhold, New York, p. 343 (1965).

164. D. C. Hess, R. R. Marshall and H. C. Urey, *Science*, **126,** 1291 (1957).

165. L. Geiling, *Z. Angew Phys.*, **3,** 467 (1951).

166. P. A. Leighton and W. G. Leighton, *J. Phys. Chem.*, **36,** 1882 (1932).

167. D. Price, *Chem. Brit.*, **4,** 255 (1968).

168. D. Price and J. E. Williams (Eds.), *Time-of-Flight Mass Spectrometry*, Pergamon Press, Oxford (1969).

169. G. V. D. Tiers, *J. Phys. Chem.*, **62,** 1151 (1958).

170. G. Milazzo and G. Cecchetti, *Appl. Spectrosc.*, **23,** 197 (1969).

171. J. T. Watson and K. Biemann, *Anal. Chem.*, **36,** 1135 (1964); **37,** 844 (1965).

172. L. Dorfman, *Chem. Rev.*, **53,** 47 (1953).

173. R. B. Woodward *et al.*, *J. Am. Chem. Soc.*, **63,** 1123, 2727 (1941); **64,** 72 (1942).

174. R. M. Dagnall, K. C. Thompson and T. S. West., *Anal. Chim. Acta*, **36,** 269 (1966).

175. C. Veillon, J. M. Mansfield, M. L. Parsons and J. D. Winefordner, *Anal. Chem.*, **38,** 205 (1966).